PREPARATION FOR
BASIC STATISTICS

A Program for
Self-instruction

McGRAW-HILL BOOK COMPANY

New York
San Francisco
St. Louis
Toronto
London
Sydney

A Program for
Self-instruction

Preparation for
Basic Statistics

Division of Biostatistics
University of California
Los Angeles

Department of Biostatistics
University of Michigan
Ann Arbor

VIRGINIA A. CLARK

MICHAEL E. TARTER

PREPARATION FOR BASIC STATISTICS
A Program for Self-instruction

Printed in the United States of America.

Library of Congress catalog card number: 67-26168

4567891011   HOCZ   7543210

Preface

This book has been designed to bridge the gap between algebra and a first-semester basic statistics course. While it is true that there need logically be no such gap, there are many reasons why one may exist: The student may need to review elementary algebra simply because of the passage of time since such a course was taken or he may have the feeling that he is inadequately prepared or simply isn't "math-oriented." The book has been written as a programmed text so that it can be used for self-study. It begins with some very simple concepts, but it does cover the mathematics needed for basic statistics courses in such fields as psychology, sociology, business, education, and public health. The idea is to save the student from having to hire a tutor or having to ask in class numerous questions that really relate to mathematics rather than statistics.

In any case, the present book emphasizes the mathematical background required for an understanding of basic statistical concepts and techniques and supplements the materials presented in a first-semester statistics course. The book should also serve as a valuable reference throughout such a course; above all mastery of the material presented will give the student the confidence and vocabulary necessary to venture forth into the world of probability, equality and inequality, digits, decimals, and descriptive formulas.

The topics covered have been divided into two broad categories. The first eight chapters include those concepts which might be introduced in an elementary algebra course, provided the course emphasized the algebra necessary for beginning statistics. For example, two of the early chapters deal with manipulations of inequalities. Modern mathematics programs now teach this concept, but unfortunately for statistics students many of the older programs neglected it. The first eight chapters should be approached sequentially; that is, the student should be familiar with the content of the earlier chapters before he covers the later ones.

The remaining five chapters deal with mathematical topics that serve isolated or "special" purposes in statistical work. For example, one chapter explains how to take the square root of a number by using tables and then systematically placing the decimal point. Another covers logarithms and the use of log graph paper. Although the order of these later chapters seems reasonable to the authors, it may be appropriate to interchange or omit several sections.

The authors hope that this text will serve as a means of reference. Whenever possible, necessary background material found earlier in the sequence has been cross-referenced in later sections to enable the reader to find it easily.

This book originated as a sequence of supplementary materials used in statistics classes at the University of California, Los Angeles. and at the University of Michigan. After the basic material was evaluated, the first version of the text was programmed; a frame-by-frame analysis was then conducted with the help of the Center for Research in Learning and Teaching at the University of Michigan and of fellow faculty and researchers at the University of California at Los Angeles. Field trials were then conducted at the University of California at Los Angeles and at the University of Michigan, as well as at the Graduate Summer Session of Statistics in the Health Sciences conducted at Yale University.

Prior to the publication of this version the text went through multiple revisions and testing. The authors are grateful to Miss Luita Swales for extensive editorial assistance, and we would also like to thank our colleagues, Professors Felix E. Moore, Wilfrid J. Dixon, Frank J. Massey, Jr., Olive Jean Dunn, and Jean Mickey, without whose help and encouragement the development of this text would have been impossible, and especially Professor Richard D. Remington, who field tested the book at Yale University.

Virginia A. Clark
Michael E. Tarter

How to Use This Book

Many spot checks have been included throughout the book, so that you will spend time on what you need to study and not on what you already know. If you are uncertain of whether or not you need to read a chapter, try the preview questions at the beginning of the chapter. If you can answer them easily, skip to the next chapter. If you cannot do them readily, go through the chapter and then check yourself by answering review questions at the end of the material. If you have problems with the review questions, repeat the chapter; if not, go on to the next one.

This book is a programmed text in which the material within chapters is presented in small, graduated steps called frames; at the end of each frame is a question to test your understanding. A question can be distinguished from its frame by the symbol ● which precedes it. Some of these questions may seem very simple, but by answering them, you check yourself and actively learn to use the concept presented in the frame. Also, immediate feedback, which tells you whether or not you understand the concept, allows you either to go ahead with confidence or to review the frame before proceeding. Two suggestions are given for using this book:

1. Write down the answer or answers to each question before checking the answers given in the gray column. Many students like to cover the margin with a piece of paper and then slip the cover down to check their answers.

2. Work for short periods of time, possibly doing a chapter at a single sitting. Upon resuming work, check your grasp of earlier material by looking at the review questions for the preceding chapter. In this way, you can use spare time periods effectively and still learn the mathematics that will make statistics easier.

Preview Questions: Chapter 1

1.1 Is a measurement of a woman's age a continuous or a discrete measurement? _____

continuous

1.2 A person's weight is 168.5 pounds.
   (*a*) What is the characteristic measured? _____
   (*b*) What is the unit of measurement? _____
   (*c*) Is this a standard unit? _____
   (*d*) Is the measurement discrete or continuous?

_____

weight
pounds
yes

continuous

1.3 Round each of the following numbers to the nearest hundredth:
   (*a*) 82.0549 _____
   (*b*) 89.0999 _____
   (*c*) 89.7705 _____
   (*d*) 87.7750 _____
   (*e*) 86.8850 _____

(*a*) 82.05
(*b*) 89.10
(*c*) 89.77
(*d*) 87.78
(*e*) 86.88

Chapter 1

Describing Measurements

This program concerns the different kinds of measurements found in statistics. In order to use statistical techniques, it is important to be able to discriminate between the types of measurements.

A method of rounding measurements is also explained in this chapter. Statistical calculations are frequently easier to perform when rounded numbers are used.

1.1   NUMBERS   All measurements are numbers. For example, an infant can be described as having a birth weight of 2,500 grams and a gestation length of 36 weeks. Two measurements are used in this description.

● Suppose during a physical examination the physician records a cholesterol level of 280 milligrams percent, a weight of 175 pounds, and a systolic blood pressure of 140 mm Hg. How many measurements are recorded? _____

three

1.2   CHARACTERISTICS   We take measurements to describe some characteristic of persons or of things. For example, the 2,500 gram birth weight describes the characteristic of weight of the infant.

● A student reports he is twenty-one years old. What is the characteristic measured? _____

age

1.3   COUNTS   One of the simplest forms of measurement is the counted measurement. Examples of counted measurements are the number of cases of typhoid fever in California in 1965 or the number of hits in a baseball game. These measurements always involve counts of people or of things. A synonym for counted measurements is enumerated measurements.

● Suppose a physician vaccinates five children against smallpox.
  (a) What is the characteristic measured? _____
  (b) What kind of measurement is it? _____

vaccination
counted (or enumerated)

1.4   DISCRETE MEASUREMENTS   Counted measurements are called discrete measurements. The number of cases of disease or the number of children in a family are examples of *discrete* measurements.

● What is the technical term for counted measurements? _____ measurements.

discrete

1.5   DISCRETE MEASUREMENTS: PRECISION   Counted measurements are the easiest measurements to make precisely. The measurements are precise because either the items being counted are there or they are not; there is little doubt about the accuracy of the measurement.

● An experiment involves three rats which weigh a total of 1.5 pounds. Which of these two measurements is likely to be more precise? _____

three rats

1.6 DISCRETE MEASUREMENTS: UNITS Discrete, or counted, measurements are never expressed as fractions. For example, there couldn't be 2½ cases of typhoid fever in a city. Discrete measurements are always whole numbers.
- Which of the following numbers might be discrete measurements? 10, ½, 112, 0.66 _____

10, 112

1.7 OTHER MEASUREMENTS Most of the work in elementary statistics deals with measurements other than counted or discrete measurements. For example, a person's height is not a discrete measurement.
- Is the blood pressure of a patient a discrete measurement? _____ Is the number of teeth a patient has a discrete measurement? _____

no
yes

1.8 UNITS OF MEASURE If we say a person's age is 15 years, his weight is 120 pounds, and his height is 5 feet, we are using years, pounds, and feet as our *units* of measurement.
- A person's temperature is 98.6°F. What is the characteristic measured? _____ Is the measurement discrete? _____ What is the unit of measurement? _____

temperature
no
degrees

1.9 STANDARD UNITS When reporting measurements, we want our results to be understood by others, so we use standard units. Standard units make it easier to compare data, and to relate our data to the practical situation. Examples of standard units are inches, days, pounds, and degrees.
- The figure below represents a ruler which has the standard unit of inches. Inches and half inches are indicated. Divide the ruler into one more unit of measurement based on a standard unit.

quarter inches

1.10 SMALLER UNITS We can divide our standard unit into smaller units by taking fractions of it. If we measure a person's height, for example, we can report the results in units of inches, or more precisely in units of half inches, or still more precisely in units of quarter inches.
- If we wish to measure height more precisely than above, then we can measure in units of _____ of an inch.

eighths

1.11 CONTINUOUS MEASUREMENTS Some kinds of measurements are called continuous measurements. A continuous measurement is one for which successive divisions of our units of measurement will give more precise measurements.

- If we measure weight, we can divide our scale into successively smaller units in order to measure more precisely. Weight is a _____ measurement.

continuous

1.12 DISCRETE MEASUREMENTS In discrete measurements it is not useful to successively divide our unit of measurement. For example, if we count 10 boys, then our unit of measurement is 1 boy of whom we have 10. Using the unit of ½ boy does not give a more precise measure.

- Would the measurement of the following things be continuous or discrete?
  (a) Height   _____
  (b) Number of mental patients
  in Ohio in 1965   _____
  (c) Number of cars in a parking
  lot   _____
  (d) Circumference of the earth   _____

continuous

discrete

discrete
continuous

1.13 CONTINUOUS MEASUREMENTS: SUBDIVISIONS When we take continuous measurements, we do not need to subdivide our scale indefinitely. We can describe the characteristic we are measuring satisfactorily after a sufficient number of subdivisions. For example, age is a continuous measurement. We call a person 14 years old up to the day he is 15, even though his age might really be 14 years, 5 months, 3 days, 1 hour, 6 minutes, and so on.

- To describe the characteristic *age* satisfactorily, we would probably call a person who is 57 years, 2 months, 10 days, 2 hours, 50 minutes, 2 seconds _____ years old.

57

1.14 ROUNDING DOWN On any day other than a birthday, the measurement we use of a person's age is *less* than his precise age. For example, any person whose age is less than 26 but greater than or equal to 25 years is called 25 years old.

- A person whose age is less than 69 years but greater than or equal to 68 years old is called _____ years old.

68

1.15 ROUNDING UP When we take a package to the post office to be weighed and postage determined, the post office uses the following procedure to determine what postage is to be charged. If the package weighs 5.2634 ounces, we will be charged for 6 ounces. We are charged for the actual weight or more.

- First class mail costs 5 cents an ounce. The cost is figured per ounce. How much will we be charged for the package weighing 5.2634 ounces? _____

30 cents

1.16 ROUNDING OFF TO NEAREST VALUE We do not measure height the way we do age or postage. Suppose it is sufficient to describe a person's height in inches. A man whose height is 70.3 inches would be called 70 inches tall. If his height were 70.8 inches, we would call him 71 inches tall. In other words, we consider a person's height to be the whole number of inches closest to his actual height. We round off to the *nearest* whole inch.

- Round off the following numbers to the nearest whole number:

  (a) 70.9 _____   (e) 70.7 _____
  (b) 70.1 _____   (f) 70.3 _____
  (c) 70.8 _____   (g) 70.6 _____
  (d) 70.2 _____   (h) 70.4 _____

(a) 71 (e) 71
(b) 70 (f) 70
(c) 71 (g) 71
(d) 70 (h) 70

1.17 ROUNDING OFF Most measurements in statistics are handled, like height, by rounding off. When we round off a number, we use *one* number to represent *many* numbers. For example, when rounding off to the nearest inch, we use 71 inches to represent *all* numbers greater than 70.5 and less than 71.5 inches.

- If we rounded off to the nearest inch, which number would we use to represent the following: 70.49, 70.30, 70.01, 69.9, 70.17? _____

70

1.18 ROUNDING OFF RULE Round off to the *closest number*. For example, when rounding off to the nearest inch, we would round off 70.51 to 71, but 70.4999 to 70. Notice that 70.51 is closer to 71, and 70.4999 is closer to 70. Notice also that 70.51 is larger than 70.4999.

- Round off the following numbers to the nearest inch:
  (a) 69.4989 _____; (b) 69.52 _____; (c) 69.01 _____.

(a) 69 (b) 70 (c) 69

1.19 ROUNDING OFF RULE Our rule that we round off to the closest number does not work when the number we wish to round off is exactly half way between the nearest two whole numbers. The rule then is to round off to the *nearest even number*. For example, 67.5 is halfway between 67 and 68. We round up to 68 because 68 is an even number. We would round 66.5 down to 66 however, because 66 is the nearest even number.

- Round off the following numbers: (a) 57.5 _____;
  (b) 76.5 _____; (c) 53.5 _____.

(a) 58
(b) 76 (c) 54

1.20 EXPLANATION OF THE ROUNDING-OFF RULE When the number to be rounded off is exactly halfway between two numbers, and we use the rule to round off to the nearest even number, we are using a method which tends to allow us to round *up* half the time and round *down* half the time. By doing this, the inaccuracies introduced by rounding tend to cancel each other out.

- Round off the following to whole numbers:
  - (*a*) 70.5 _____
  - (*b*) 71.5 _____
  - (*c*) 72.5 _____
  - (*d*) 73.5 _____
  - (*e*) 74.5 _____
  - (*f*) 75.5 _____

(*a*) 70 (*d*) 74
(*b*) 72 (*e*) 74
(*c*) 72 (*f*) 76

1.21 ROUNDING OFF TO LARGER NUMBERS We do not always round off to the nearest whole number. Measurements can be rounded to the nearest tens, or hundreds, or thousands. For example, if the population of a city at the time of a census is 273,126, this number can be rounded off to 273,000. Notice that 273,126 is rounded off to the nearest thousand.

- Round off 729,832 to the nearest thousand. _____

730,000

1.22 ROUNDING OFF TO LARGER NUMBERS Many measurements will be represented by the same rounded-off number when we round to larger numbers. For example, all numbers between 788,501 and 789,499, inclusive, can be rounded off to 789,000. As another example, the number 126,000 can be used to *represent* all numbers between 125,500 and 126,500, inclusive.

- Round off the following to the nearest thousand:
  - (*a*) 111,540 _____; (*b*) 2,006 _____;
  - (*c*) 123,500 _____.

(*a*) 112,000
(*b*) 2,000
(*c*) 124,000

Review: Chapter 1

1.1 Are the following measurements discrete or continuous?
  (*a*) Census population of New York City _____
  (*b*) Birth weight of an infant _____
  (*c*) Litter size _____
  (*d*) Length of time it takes a rocket to rise 100 feet _____

discrete

continuous
discrete

continuous

1.2 In reporting data it is important to use standard _____ of measurement so that other people can understand your results.

units

1.3   If dividing our scale into successively smaller units enables us to measure more precisely, then we are making a _____ measurement.

continuous

1.4   Round off the following numbers to the nearest whole numbers:

(*a*) 71.6925 _____   (*d*) 68.5   _____
(*b*) 80.1   _____   (*e*)   0.689 _____
(*c*) 21.234   _____   (*f*) 13.500 _____

(*a*) 72   (*d*) 68
(*b*) 80   (*e*)   1
(*c*) 21   (*f*) 14

1.5   Round off the following numbers to the nearest hundredth: (a) 71.6925 _____; (b) 80.555 _____;
(c) 21.11111 _____.

(*a*) 71.69
(*b*) 80.56
(*c*) 21.11

1.6   Report the following ages by year, using the traditional method of rounding ages.

(*a*) 55.6 years   _____
(*b*) 21.5 years   _____
(*c*) 16.9 years   _____
(*d*) 78.5 years   _____
(*e*) 3 years, 3 months   _____
(*f*) 10 years, 9 months _____

(*a*) 55
(*b*) 21
(*c*) 16
(*d*) 78
(*e*)   3
(*f*) 10

1.7   In the preceding problem, is the measurement rounded to the *nearest* whole number? _____

no

1.8   A person's height is 68⅜ inches.
(*a*) What is the characteristic measured? _____
(*b*) What is the unit of measurement? _____
(*c*) Is the measurement discrete or continuous?
_____

height
inches

continuous

Preview Questions: Chapter 2

2.1   Suppose one is measuring the number of phone calls received on consecutive days. There were no calls, then 3 calls, and then 8 calls. How many measurements were taken?
_____

three

2.2   Suppose the number sequence obtained in the preceding question is 3, 3, 3, 5, 5, 5, 5. How many measurements were taken? _____

seven

2.3   Is $-13°C > -14°C$? _____

yes

2.4   On the number scale below, does the arrow point to a positive or negative number? _____

negative

0

2.5   Given the set of observations 8, 81, 17, what would X_n be? _____

$X_n = 17$

2.6   Consider two statements:
    Statement 1: $X_1 = 15$ and $X_2 = 15$
    Statement 2: $X_1 = 15$ and $X_1 = 16$
(*a*) Both statements are impossible.
(*b*) 1 is possible, but 2 is impossible.
(*c*) 1 is impossible, but 2 is possible.
(*d*) Both statements are possible.

(*b*)

2.7   From the symbols *j*, *Y*, or *b*, choose suitable letters to represent:
(*a*) An arbitrary observation. _____
(*b*) A subscript. _____
(*c*) A nonchangeable number. _____

Y
j
b

2.8   For $X_1 = 2$, $X_2 = 4$, $X_3 = 2$, compute

$$\sum_{i=1}^{n} X_i = \underline{\quad}$$

8

2.9   For the same observations compute

$$\sum_{i=2}^{n-1} X_i = \underline{\quad}$$

4

Chapter 2

Number
and Symbol
Vocabulary

In this chapter the number vocabulary is extended to include zero and negative numbers. The operations of addition and subtraction of positive and negative numbers are reviewed, and the relationships "less than" and "greater than," with their respective symbols, are illustrated.

In the second section, the use of symbols to represent kinds of numbers and the use of subscripted symbols are considered. In the final section, use of the summation sign Σ is discussed and illustrated.

A: ZERO AND NEGATIVE NUMBERS

2.1   POSITIVE NUMBERS   In the previous chapter on measurement you learned about discrete measurements which occur as positive whole numbers (such as 10; 3; 2,501). You also learned about continuous measurements which are expressed as positive whole numbers or as fractions or decimals (such as 11, $^{15}/_{16}$, or 0.234). The number vocabulary in the last program on measurement only included *positive* numbers.

●   Positive numbers are always _____ than zero.

greater (or larger)

2.2   ZERO   Frequently we associate the number zero with a measurement. For example, the freezing point of an unknown liquid may be measured and found to be 0°C. A measurement with a value zero is considered an observation just as a measurement with a value of 10 would be.

●   If, in successive games, a team scores 1, 0, and 3 goals, how many numbers are listed to describe the number of goals scored? _____

three

2.3   COUNTS   Very often in statistics it is necessary to count the number of observations or measurements. If we make two observations and obtain the same measurement value both times, the number of observations is still two, even though their value is the same.

●   Each of the following numbers represents one observation: 2, 4, 0, 1, 0, 6, 1. How many observations were made? _____

seven

2.4   NEGATIVE NUMBERS   In general, most of our observations are positive numbers and our final results positive numbers, but we frequently use negative numbers in the process of *calculating* our answers.

●   Frequently we measure with _____ numbers but use _____ numbers in our calculations.

positive
negative

2.5   NEGATIVE NUMBERS   Sometimes the measurements themselves are negative numbers. For example, using a centigrade thermometer to measure temperatures sometimes results in negative numbers. Zero is set at the freezing point of distilled water. If we measure the freezing point of salt water, using this thermometer, we will need a negative number to represent this measurement.

●   When we measure the freezing point of antifreeze solution, using a centigrade thermometer, this freezing point will be a _____ number.

negative

2.6   NUMBER SCALE   Thinking of a centigrade thermometer
scale is useful when interpreting positive and negative numbers.

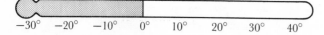

Notice that the number zero separates the positive numbers
from the negative numbers.

●   Suppose we immerse our thermometer into a solution
and read 0°C. Then, if we heat the solution and again
measure the temperature, the temperature will be a
_____ number. If we cool the solution until its
temperature is below 0°C, then the temperature measurement will be a _____ number.

positive

negative

2.7   SIZE OF NEGATIVE NUMBERS   A temperature of $-20°C$
is colder than a temperature of $-10°C$. We can see that
$-20°C$ is represented by a point which is *to the left* of $-10°C$.
If the first number is to the left of the second number, then
the first number is *less than* the second number if we have a
number scale such as a thermometer.

●   (*a*) A temperature of $-12°C$ is to the _____ of
      $-8°C$.
      (*b*) Which number is less, -16 or -21? ____
      (*c*) Which number is less, -2 or 0? ____
      (*d*) Is 0 less than 5? _____
      (*e*) Is -6 less than -8? _____

left

-21
-2
yes
no

2.8   ARITHMETIC INVOLVING NEGATIVE NUMBERS   Negative
numbers can be added, subtracted, multiplied, and divided just
like positive ones. To add negative numbers forget about the
signs, and add their absolute values, then prefix the answer
with a minus sign. (Note that the absolute value of -3 is 3.)

● $-3 - 7 =$ ____
      $-1 - 10 =$ ____

-10
-11

2.9   ADDITION OF NUMBERS   To add two numbers with unlike signs (one positive and one negative), *subtract* the smaller
absolute value from the larger absolute value and prefix the
answer with the sign of the number with the larger absolute
value. For example, to add -5 and $+3$, choose 5 as the
larger value and compute $5 - 3$. The result is 2, and since
the larger value had a minus sign, the answer is -2.

● $-3 - 7 =$ ____ $+0 - 6 =$ ____
      $-3 + 7 =$ ____ $+6 - 6 =$ ____
      $+3 - 7 =$ ____

-10 -6
4   0
-4

2.10   SUBTRACTION OF NEGATIVE NUMBERS   To subtract a
negative number from another number (which may be either

positive or negative), change the sign of the one you are subtracting to plus, then the problem becomes one of addition.
For example, to subtract -2 from -6, change the sign of
-2 to $+$, then add: $-6 + 2 = -4$.

- Subtract: -4 from $-8 =$ _____ -4
  Subtract: -4 from $0 =$ _____ $+4$
  Subtract: -4 from $+4 =$ _____ $+8$

2.11   PARENTHESES   Parentheses are often used to set apart
a negative number with its sign. For example, -2 can be
written as (-2). Then operations of addition and subtraction involving negative numbers can be written as follows:
$(+3) + (-2) = (+1)$. This is read as "plus three plus minus
two equals plus one," or as "three plus minus two equals one."

-    $(+4) + (-2) =$ _____ $+2$
     $(4) - \quad (2) =$ _____ 2
     $(-3) - (-3) =$ _____ 0
     $(-3) + (-3) =$ _____ -6

2.12   INEQUALITIES: THE "LESS THAN" SIGN   In statistics the
concept "less than" is often used, so it is valuable to have a
symbol to represent these words. The symbol for "less than"
is related to the symbol for "equals," or $=$. If we pinch together the left-hand side of two bars of the equality sign, we
obtain the less than or inequality sign, $<$.

- Write the symbols for the phrase "5 is less than 8." $5 < 8$
  _____

2.13   INEQUALITIES: THE "GREATER THAN" SIGN   The symbol
for "greater than" is just the opposite of the symbol for "less
than." The pinched end of the inequality sign points to the
right. The statement that "10 is greater than 3" can be written as $10 > 3$. An additional way of writing the previous
statement is $3 < 10$.

- Write the symbols for the phrase "8 is greater than 5." $8 > 5$
  _____ Write out the statement represented by the
  following symbols: $-3°C > -4°C$. $-3°C$ is greater than
       $-4°C$

2.14   TWO INEQUALITIES   Often we use two inequality signs
in the same statement. If we want to say that $-1°C$ is less
than $0°C$, and $0°C$ is less than $1°C$, we write this in symbols
as $-1°C < 0°C < 1°C$.

- (a) Write out the symbols for the statement "-3 is
  less than -1, and -1 is less than 0." _____   (a) $-3 < -1 < 0$
  (b) Reverse this statement, and use the "greater than"
  symbol. _____   (b) $0 > -1 > -3$
  (c) Write out in words what the symbols in part b
  mean _____   (c)   0 is greater than
       -1, and -1 is
       greater than -3

2.15 EXAMPLE OF POSITIVE AND NEGATIVE NUMBERS: TIME
If we think of the present as "time 0," then an event which
happened three hours ago can be designated as happening at
−3 hours. An event which happened one hour ago happened
at −1 hours. The time two hours in the future can be designated as +2 hours.

● Using the "less than" symbol, write the symbols for this
statement: An event which happened two hours ago
occurred before an event which happened one hour
ago. _____

$-2 \text{ hours} < -1 \text{ hour}$

B: SYMBOL VOCABULARY

Up to now, whenever we discussed numbers, we used
either words or numerals such as −5, 3, or 0. In this section
we will introduce the use of symbols. Symbols will enable us
to handle numbers more conveniently.

2.16 SYMBOLS Suppose we want to measure a man's weight.
We could write down our answer as "the man's weight = 160
pounds," or we could use a *symbol*, and write "$W = 160$
pounds." Here W stands for "the man's weight."

● Use Y as a symbol to represent height, and write down
the statement that "the man's height is 70 inches."

_____

$Y = 70 \text{ in.}$

2.17 SUBSCRIPTED SYMBOLS If we measured the weight of
three men, we could let W stand for the first man's weight,
Y for the second man's weight, and Z for the third man's
weight. But if we measured a large number of weights, we
would soon run out of letters of the alphabet to use as our
symbols. To avoid this difficulty, and to give us a method of
keeping track of which man's weight we are talking about (the
first, second, or tenth), we use *subscripted* symbols.

● Using the alphabet alone, would we have enough letters
for 60 distinct symbols? _____

no

2.18 SUBSCRIPTED SYMBOLS: EXAMPLE Subscripted symbols
give us a method of obtaining an unlimited number of symbols and of keeping track of the order of our observations.
Suppose we measure the weight of four men, and obtain the
following results:

First man's weight = 154 pounds
Second man's weight = 189 pounds
Third man's weight = 206 pounds
Fourth man's weight = 162 pounds

Instead of writing "first man's weight" we can write W_1. This is read as "W sub 1" and represents the weight of the first man. To represent the weight of the second man, we can write W_2.

● What subscripted symbol can we use to represent the weight of the third man? _____ The symbol W_4 represents the weight of the _____ man, and is read aloud as W _____ 4.

W_3
fourth
sub

2.19 SUBSCRIPTED SYMBOLS: EXAMPLE The heights of three men can be written as $X_1 = 72$ inches, $X_2 = 69$ inches, and $X_3 = 70$ inches.

● The height in numbers for the second man is _____. The symbol for the first man's height is _____.

69 in.
X_1

2.20 THE SYMBOL n The letter n is used as a symbol to denote the *total number of observations*. If we take 10 measurements, then $n = 10$.

● For the observations,
$$W_1 = 154 \text{ pounds}$$
$$W_2 = 189 \text{ pounds}$$
$$W_3 = 206 \text{ pounds}$$
$$W_4 = 162 \text{ pounds}$$
$$n = \underline{\hspace{2cm}}.$$

four

2.21 THE SUBSCRIPT n The letter n can also be used as a subscript. It denotes the last, or the nth observation. In the previous problem, W_4 can also be written as W_n. Thus $W_4 = W_n$.

● If we had a total of six observations, then $W_6 =$ _____. If we had a total of 10 measurements, write down the two symbols which would stand for the last measurement. _____ and _____.

W_n

W_n W_{10}

2.22 ARBITRARY SUBSCRIPTS We have already used subscripted symbols to represent *particular* measurements, such as W_1 to represent the first man's weight and W_n to represent the last man's weight. To represent an arbitrary weight, any one between the first and the last, inclusive, we often use the subscript i. Thus W_i stands for the weight of any member in the group, and i can be any number from 1 to n, inclusive.

● To represent the weight of the second man, we use the symbol _____, where _____ is the subscript. To represent the weight of the last man, we use the symbol _____, where _____ is the subscript. To represent an arbitrary measurement of weight, we use the symbol _____, where _____ is the subscript.

W_2 2

W_n n

W_i i

2.23 ARBITRARY SUBSCRIPTS: EXAMPLE Suppose we measure the temperatures of three patients:

$$X_1 = 98.9° = \text{first patient's temperature}$$
$$X_2 = 100.2° = \text{second patient's temperature}$$
$$X_3 = 98.6° = \text{third patient's temperature}$$

We use the symbol X_i to denote the temperature of the ith patient, when we are not interested in whether he is the first or the second or the third.

●   In the example above, how many values can the subscript i take on? _____ What are the possible values of i? _____ In referring to the temperature of the second patient, i takes on the value _____.

three
1, 2, 3
2

2.24 OTHER ARBITRARY SUBSCRIPTS We have used the letter i to represent an arbitrary subscript. The letters j and k are also conventionally used in this manner. Thus the symbols X_i, X_j, and X_k can all refer to an arbitrary observation.

●   The symbol W_i stands for an arbitrary observation. What other two symbols could be used? _____ and _____

W_j
W_k

2.25 SYMBOLS FOR OBSERVATIONS To represent different types of observations, the symbols W_i, X_i, and Y_i are commonly used. For example, the symbol X_i might represent the height of an arbitrary person, the symbol W_i might represent his weight, and the symbol Y_i might represent his age. Notice that the letters W, X, and Y come at the end of the alphabet.

●   Besides W, X, and Y, choose another symbol which could be used for different types of observations. _____

$Z, U,$ or V

2.26 SYMBOLS FOR CONSTANTS We have used letters in the middle of the alphabet to represent subscripts (i, j, k, and n) and letters at the end of the alphabet to represent observations (W, X, Y, Z). We use letters at the beginning of the alphabet to represent numbers, called *constants*, which do not change in the course of a single problem. Constant numbers can be represented by the symbols a, b, and c.

●   From a, i, X_i, or Y_n choose suitable symbols to represent:

     (a) An arbitrary observation. _____
     (b) A subscript. _____
     (c) The last observation. _____
     (d) A nonchangeable number. _____

(a) X_i
(b) i
(c) Y_n
(d) a

C: THE ADDITION SYMBOL

2.27 SUMS To write the sum of three observations in symbols, where $X_1 = 10$ pounds, $X_2 = 12$ pounds, and $X_3 = 13$ pounds, we would write:
$$X_1 + X_2 + X_3 = 10 + 12 + 13 = 35 \text{ pounds}$$
- Write the symbols, and the answer, for the sum of the first two observations. _____ = _____

$X_1 + X_2 = 22 \text{ lb}$

2.28 SUM OF A SERIES OF NUMBERS Suppose we want to write out the sum of 100 observations in symbols. We can write this sum as
$$X_1 + X_2 + X_3 + \cdots + X_{99} + X_{100}$$
where the dots stand for the observations we haven't written down.
- The expression $X_1 + X_2 + \cdots + X_{24} + X_{25}$ represents the sum of _____ numbers.

25

2.29 THE Σ SIGN Instead of writing out the symbolic expression for the sum of numbers, we can use the symbol Σ to represent the phrase "the sum of." The symbol Σ is the capital form of the Greek letter *sigma* which is like our S and is an abbreviation of the word "sum." The symbol Σ is read aloud as "sigma."
- The symbol Σ is used to represent the phrase

_____.

"the sum of"

2.30 SUMMATION SIGN WITH SUBSCRIPTS Instead of writing a symbol for each observation and using plus signs to indicate addition, we can use the symbol Σ, which means "the sum of." For example, instead of writing $X_1 + X_2 + X_3 + X_4$, we use the expression ΣX_i. But we must indicate the values of the subscript i that we are summing over. In this example, i goes from 1 to 4, thus the expression for the sum of the four numbers is
$$\sum_{i=1}^{4} X_i$$
This is read in words as "the sum of X_i for i equals one to four." Note that
$$\sum_{i=1}^{4} X_i = X_1 + X_2 + X_3 + X_4$$
- Write the expression for $Y_1 + Y_2 + Y_3$, using the Σ sign and the symbol Y_i to represent an arbitrary observation. _____ Write out another way to indicate $\sum_{i=1}^{2} X_i$. _____ $\sum_{i=1}^{4} Y_i$ is read in words as _____

$\sum_{i=1}^{3} Y_i$

$X_1 + X_2$

The sum of Y_i for i equals 1 to 4.

2.31 USE OF THE SUMMATION SIGN: EXAMPLE If we have found the ages of four children to be

$$Y_1 = 5 \text{ years} = \text{age of first child}$$
$$Y_2 = 6 \text{ years} = \text{age of second child}$$
$$Y_3 = 4 \text{ years} = \text{age of third child}$$
$$Y_4 = 5 \text{ years} = \text{age of fourth child}$$

then

$$\sum_{i=1}^{4} Y_i = Y_1 + Y_2 + Y_3 + Y_4 = 20$$

● Suppose we had only measured the ages of the first three children. Write out the symbols for the sum of their ages. ——————— What is the numerical value of this sum? ———————

$$\sum_{i=1}^{3} Y_i$$

15 years

2.32 SUBSCRIPT VALUES ON THE SYMBOL Σ The values of the subscripts which appear below and above the Σ symbol tell us which of the observations to include in the sum. Thus $\sum_{i=1}^{5} X_i$ means the sum of $X_1 + X_2 + X_3 + X_4 + X_5$. We would indicate the sum of $X_2 + X_3 + X_4$ as $\sum_{i=2}^{4} X_i$. The value of the subscript which appears below the Σ tells us which observation to start the addition with, and the value which appears above the Σ tells us the last observation to include in the sum.

● Suppose we have the following measurements:
   $Y_1 = 3 \qquad Y_2 = 4 \qquad Y_3 = 1 \qquad Y_4 = 5 \qquad Y_5 = 3$
   (a) What is the numerical value of

   $$\sum_{i=1}^{n} Y_i? \quad \underline{\qquad}$$

   (b) What is n in this case? ———
   (c) What is the symbol for $Y_2 + Y_3 + Y_4 + Y_5$?
   ———————
   (d) What is the symbol for $Y_1 + Y_2$? ———————

(a) 16

(b) 5

(c) $\sum_{i=2}^{5} Y_i$

(d) $\sum_{i=1}^{2} Y_i$

2.33 USE OF SUBSCRIPTS Many statistical texts do *not* include the expression above and below the summation sign. For example, instead of writing

$$\sum_{i=1}^{n} X_i$$

they use ΣX, and in this abbreviated terminology it is understood that all X_i values from X_1 to X_n are added.

● If $X_1 = 1$, $X_2 = 2$, and $X_3 = 5$, what is ΣX? ———.

8

Review: Chapter 2

2.1 Which of the following are positive numbers? 3.6, ⅕, −0.13 _____

2.2 Two experiments are performed. In experiment 1 the observations 1, 0, 3, 3, 0, 0, 2, 3 are obtained, and in experiment 2 the observations 7, 6, 8, 9, 11, 6, 21 are obtained. In which experiment are more observations made?

_____

experiment 1

2.3 The symbols a and b represent two numbers placed on a number scale:

According to the conventional definition of the number scale, which symbol represents the smaller number? _____

a

2.4 Perform the following calculations:
●
  (*a*) $-6 + 3 =$ _____
  (*b*) $(-6) + (-6) =$ _____
  (*c*) $0 - 4 =$ _____
  (*d*) $(-2 + 4) =$ _____

(*a*) -3
(*b*) -12
(*c*) -4
(*d*) 2

2.5 If $X < Y < Z$, then which symbol represents (*a*) the largest number? _____ (*b*) the phrase "is less than"? _____

Z $<$

2.6 What is the symbol which represents the phrase "is greater than"? _____

$>$

2.7 If $W_1 = 5$ pounds and $W_2 = 1$ pound, which is larger, W_1 or W_2? _____

W_1

2.8 (*a*) We use letters toward the _____ of the alphabet to represent subscripts.
  (*b*) We use letters toward the _____ of the alphabet to represent observations.
  (*c*) We use letters toward the _____ of the alphabet to represent constants (nonchanging numbers).

(*a*) middle

(*b*) end

(*c*) beginning

2.9 We are given the following observations: 156, 97, 131, 137.
●
  (*a*) What is n? _____
  (*b*) What is W_n? _____

(*a*) 4
(*b*) 137

2.10   The symbol W_i represents the weight of the ith person from the first to the nth, inclusive.   Suppose four observations are taken.

●   (a) How many values can be assumed by the symbol i?

_____

(b) What is the largest possible value of i?   _____
(c) What is the value of n?   _____
(d) Is W_4 necessarily the largest possible value of W_i?

_____

(a) 4
(b) 4
(c) 4

(d) no

2.11   For $X_1 = 10$ pounds, $X_2 = 15$ pounds, and $X_3 = 20$ pounds, compute the following sums:

●   (a) $\sum\limits_{i=1}^{3} X_i = $ _____

(a) 45 lb

(b) $\sum\limits_{i=1}^{2} X_i = $ _____

(b) 25 lb

(c) $\sum\limits_{i=2}^{3} X_i = $ _____

(c) 35 lb

Preview Questions: Chapter 3

3.1 Write three different equations which state that X and Y are equal. _____, _____, and _____.

$$X = Y \qquad X - Y = 0$$
$$X/Y = 1$$

3.2 Compute $(8)(2 + 3) =$ ____.

40

3.3 Compute

$$\frac{15}{4 + 1} = \underline{\hspace{1cm}}$$

3

3.4 Compute

$$\frac{2 + 8}{1 + 4} = \underline{\hspace{1cm}}$$

2

3.5 If $X_1 = 5$, $X_2 = 15$, and $X_3 = 10$, then $\overline{X} =$ ____.

10

3.6 Given $X_1 = 2$ and $X_2 = 4$, compute the sample variance

$$S^2 = \frac{\sum_{i=1}^{n} (X_i - \overline{X})^2}{n - 1} = \underline{\hspace{1cm}}$$

2

Chapter **3**

Manipulating Symbols and Numbers

The first section of this chapter reviews the definition of equations. In this section, symbols will be used to stand for numbers. If you need further background on the use of symbols, review Section B of Chapter 2. In the second section of this chapter, the manipulation of equations is discussed.

A: EQUATIONS AND EQUALITY

3.1   EQUATION SENTENCE   So far we have built up a vocabulary of symbols and numbers. Words are combined in sentences. Symbols and numbers will be combined in equations. For example, we can write, using word vocabulary, two plus two equals four, or, using symbol and number vocabulary, $2 + 2 = 4$.

- Instead of the sentence, three minus two equals one, we can write the equation _____.

$3 - 2 = 1$

3.2   EQUATION   An equation is a symbolic way of writing a sentence whose main verb is "equals."

- In the equation $X = Y + 6$, the verb is expressed symbolically as _____.

$=$

3.3   EQUALITY   Just as there are many sentences that say the same thing, there are at least three equations that can be used to express the concept that one quantity is the same as another quantity. To express in symbols the sentence, "The measurement X equals the measurement Y," we can write $X = Y$.

- Assuming that two observations, X_i and X_j, are the same, write an equation which expresses the relationship. _____

$X_i = X_j$

3.4   EQUALITY   If $X = Y$, there is no difference between the measurement X and the measurement Y. If you subtract Y from X, the answer is zero.

- Write this subtraction in equation form. _____

$X - Y = 0$

3.5   EQUALITY   If you have a fraction whose numerator and denominator are the same, then this fraction must equal 1. For example, $23/23 = 1$. The value of a fraction equals 1 only when the numerator and denominator are equal. (The numerator is the top part of a fraction; the denominator is the bottom part.)

- If $X/Y = 1$, then we know that $X =$ _____.

Y

3.6   EQUALITY   If there are 10 children in ward A, and if 10 children in ward A have measles, then we can write the fraction,

$$\frac{10 \text{ children with measles}}{10 \text{ children}} = \frac{10}{10} = 1$$

- Does the number of children who have measles equal the number of children in the ward? _____

yes

3.7   REVIEW   Let's review the three equations which express the sentence, "The measurements X and Y are equal." These are $X = Y$, $X - Y = 0$, and $X/Y = 1$.

- Suppose we know that $X + A = Y$. Express this equality in two other ways.

    _____ and _____

B: OPERATIONS

3.8   OPERATION OF ADDITION AND SUBTRACTION   In the equation $X - Y = 0$, the operation that links X and Y is subtraction.

- In the equation $X + Y = 0$, the operation that links X and Y is _____.

addition

3.9   OPERATION OF MULTIPLICATION   Parentheses are used to separate numbers which will be multiplied together.   For example, 5 times 6 is written as $(5)(6) = 30$.

- Write the equation, 82 times 11 equals 902, using parentheses.   _____

$(82)(11) = 902$

3.10   OPERATION OF MULTIPLICATION   When the numbers to be multiplied are both positive, the answer is positive.   When the numbers to be multiplied are both negative, the answer is again positive.   But when one number is negative and one number is positive, the answer is negative.

- (a) $(-1)(-2) =$ ____
- (b) $(3)(3) =$ ____
- (c) $(-3)(-3) =$ ____
- (d) $(-1)(1) =$ ____
- (e) $(4)(-3) =$ ____

(a) 2
(b) 9
(c) 9
(d) −1
(e) −12

3.11   OPERATION OF MULTIPLICATION   When we wish to multiply *symbols*, we write the symbols next to each other.   As words, the expression XY is read as "X times Y" or "X multiplied by Y."

- Write the expression for X times Y times Z.   _____

XYZ

3.12   OPERATION OF DIVISION   In the equation $X/Y = Z$, the operation that links X and Y is division.   The symbol / is called a division bar.   The operation X/Y is read as "X divided by Y."

- 50 divided by 10 can be written as ____ = ____. Write the equation for equality of X and Y using the division bar.   _____.

$50/10 = 5$

$X/Y = 1$

3.13   PARENTHESES IN ORDERING   To add two numbers together and then multiply the results by a third number, we use parentheses.   Parentheses determine the *order* of performing operations. For example, the expression "(2 plus 4) times 7" equals (6) times 7, or 42. We *combine* the numbers within the parentheses and then use this combination as a single number in further calculations.

- $6(3 + 2)$ equals $(\underline{})(\underline{}) = \underline{}$.

$(6)(5) = 30$

3.14 ORDER OF OPERATIONS It is important to perform operations in the correct order. For example, $(2)(10 + 4) = (2)(14) = 28$, since numbers within the parentheses must be combined before they are operated on outside the parentheses.

- Calculate $(3 + 6)(2) = \underline{}$, $(3)(6) + 2 = \underline{}$, and $3 + (6)(2) = \underline{}$.

18 20
15

3.15 DIVISION BAR IN ORDERING The order of operations is determined by the division bar, as well as by parentheses. In most calculations, it is advisable to perform all the computations separately on either side of the division bar before doing the division. For example, in calculating

$$\frac{20}{4 + 36} = \frac{20}{40} = \frac{1}{2}$$

we first add 4 and 36 together, and then divide. Also, $\frac{4 + 6}{2 + 8}$ is the same as $(4 + 6)/(2 + 8)$.

- In the following expression, combine together, using parentheses, the two terms which will be computed before division.

$$\frac{3 + 10}{6 + 6 + 1} = \underline{}$$

$(3 + 10)/(6 + 6 + 1)$

3.16 COMBINING To obtain a numerically correct answer in division, combine all the numbers in the numerator and separately combine all the numbers in the denominator. For example,

$$\frac{(10)(12)}{59 + 1} = \frac{120}{60} = 2$$

- $\dfrac{(3)(4) + 3}{4 + 1} = \underline{}$

3

3.17 AVERAGE The rule stated in frame 3.15 can be used to compute the average (arithmetic mean) of a group of numbers. Suppose we have five observations, $X_1 = 2$, $X_2 = 3$, $X_3 = 4$, $X_4 = 8$, $X_5 = 3$. The formula for the average is

$$\frac{\sum_{i=1}^{n} X_i}{n}$$

where n is the number of observations (in this case 5). The $\sum_{i=1}^{n} X_i$ is read, "the sum of X_i for $i = 1$ to n." Because of the division bar, we will sum the five numbers before we divide by 5. The average will be

$$\frac{2 + 3 + 4 + 8 + 3}{5} = \frac{20}{5} = 4$$

- In the following expression, put parentheses around the term which will be computed before division:

$$\frac{\sum\limits_{i=1}^{n} X_i}{n}$$

$$\left(\sum\limits_{i=1}^{n} X_i \right)$$

3.18 SYMBOL FOR MEAN Instead of writing the word *mean* or *average*, we can use the symbol $\overline{X}$. This symbol is read as "X bar."

- Fill in the missing symbol in the following:

$$\underline{\quad\quad} = \frac{\sum\limits_{i=1}^{n} X_i}{n}$$

$$\overline{X}$$

$$\underline{\quad\quad} = \frac{\sum\limits_{i=1}^{n} Y_i}{n}$$

$$\overline{Y}$$

3.19 FORMULA A formula is an equation which can be used to express a rule, fact, or definition. For example, the formula for the mean, $\overline{X}$, is defined to be

$$\overline{X} = \frac{\sum\limits_{i=1}^{n} X_i}{n}$$

- Which of the following is a formula: (a) $e = mc^2$; (b) e/mc^2; (c) $(e^2 + m)c$? $\underline{\quad\quad}$

$(a)\ e = mc^2$

3.20 VARIANCE FORMULA Besides the formula for the mean, other formulas will be used in statistics. One of these formulas is the formula for the variance. By definition, the sample variance formula is

$$\text{Variance} = \frac{\sum\limits_{i=1}^{n} (X_i - \overline{X})^2}{n - 1}$$

- In the variance formula, which symbol is used to represent the phrase "the sum of"? $\underline{\quad\quad}$ Which symbol represents the sample size? $\underline{\quad\quad}$ For which symbol appearing in the variance formula have we already learned a formula? $\underline{\quad\quad}$

Σ

n

$\overline{X}$

3.21 SYMBOL FOR VARIANCE Instead of writing the word *variance* we can use the symbol S^2.

● Fill in the missing symbol in the following:

$$\rule{1.5cm}{0.4pt} = \frac{\sum_{i=1}^{n} (X_i - \overline{X})^2}{n - 1}$$

S^2

3.22 SQUARING A shorthand way of writing $(5)(5)$ is 5^2. In symbols, $(X)(X) = XX = X^2$.

● A shorthand way of writing $(X_i - \overline{X})(X_i - \overline{X})$ is

$\rule{3cm}{0.4pt}$.

$(X_i - \overline{X})^2$

3.23 SQUARING We read 5^2 as "five squared." We would read $(X_i - X)^2$ as "X_i minus $\overline{X}$ *quantity* squared."

● We read $(Y_i - \overline{Y})^2$ as $\rule{4cm}{0.4pt}$

$\rule{8cm}{0.4pt}$.

Y_i minus $\overline{Y}$ quantity squared

3.24 SQUARING Since we have parentheses around $X_i - \overline{X}$, we first compute the quantity $(X_i - \overline{X})$.

● If $X_i = 5$ and $\overline{X} = 4$, to compute S^2 we first compute $(X_i - \overline{X}) = \rule{1cm}{0.4pt}$.

1

3.25 SQUARING After we have computed the quantity inside the parentheses, $(X_i - \overline{X})$, we next square $(X_i - \overline{X})$.

● If $X_1 = 1$, $X_2 = 3$, and $n = 2$, then $\overline{X} = \rule{1cm}{0.4pt}$.
$(X_1 - \overline{X}) = \rule{1cm}{0.4pt}$ and $(X_2 - \overline{X}) = \rule{1cm}{0.4pt}$.
$(X_1 - \overline{X})^2 = \rule{1cm}{0.4pt}$ and $(X_2 - \overline{X})^2 = \rule{1cm}{0.4pt}$.
$\sum_{i=1}^{2} (X_1 - \overline{X})^2 = (X_1 - \overline{X})^2 + (X_2 - \overline{X})^2 = \rule{1cm}{0.4pt}$.

2
−1 1
1 1

2

3.26 COMPUTATION OF VARIANCE Since the division bar separates the numerator and denominator, once we have computed

$$\sum_{i=1}^{n} (X_i - \overline{X})^2$$

we divide it by the quantity $n - 1$ to get the variance S^2.

● If $X_1 = 1$, $X_2 = 3$, and $n = 2$, what is the numerical value of

$$S^2 = \frac{\sum_{i=1}^{2} (X_i - \overline{X})^2}{n - 1} = \rule{1cm}{0.4pt}$$

2

Review: Chapter 3

3.1 Fill in the missing parts of the following equations. Each of these equations expresses the concept that one quantity, X_1, is the same as another quantity, X_2.

$$X_1 \underline{\quad\quad} X_2$$
$$X_1 - X_2 = \underline{\quad\quad}$$
$$\frac{X_1}{X_2} = \underline{\quad\quad}$$

$=$

0

1

3.2 We know $(2)(3) = 6$. Therefore we can write $(2)(3) - 6 = \underline{\quad\quad}$.

0

3.3 We know, therefore, that the difference between $(2)(3)$ and 6 is $\underline{\quad\quad}$.

0

3.4 If the difference between two quantities is equal to zero, then the two quantities are $\underline{\quad\quad\quad}$.

equal

3.5 $(2)(11) - 6 = \underline{\quad\quad}$.

16

3.6 If we want to perform an addition before a multiplication, then we use $\underline{\quad\quad\quad}$.

parentheses

3.7 $2(11 - 6) = \underline{\quad\quad}$.

10

3.8 In the equation $10/10 = 1$, the symbol separating the two 10's is called a $\underline{\quad\quad\quad}$ bar.

division

3.9 $\dfrac{3 + 9}{2 + 2} = \underline{\quad\quad}$.

3

3.10 Write with symbols an equation which corresponds to the sentence, (ten plus five) divided by (two plus three) equals three. $\underline{\quad\quad\quad\quad\quad}$

$$\frac{10 + 5}{2 + 3} = 3$$

3.11 What is the symbol for the mean? $\underline{\quad\quad}$

$\overline{X}$

3.12 What is the symbol for the variance? $\underline{\quad\quad}$

S^2

Preview Questions: Chapter 4

4.1 If $X_1 = X_2 = X_3 = \cdots X_i = \cdots X_{10} = 15$, then

$$\sum_{i=1}^{10} X_i = \underline{\hspace{1cm}}$$

150

4.2 If we use standard statistical notation and the observations given are 8, 8, 5, 5, 5, 4, 4, 4, 2, 2, 2, 2, 2, then $f_2 = \underline{\hspace{1cm}}$.

3

4.3 Compute

$$\sum_{i=2}^{c} f_i X_i^2 = \underline{\hspace{1cm}}$$

66

where $c = 2$ and the observations given are 3, 3, 4, 4, 4.

4.4 Which number or numbers appearing in the following expression is (are) a common factor?

$$2(8+1) + 2(8+15) + 2(8+9) \underline{\hspace{1cm}}$$

2

4.5 Which of the following statements are true?

(a) $A \sum_{i=1}^{n} X_i < \sum_{i=1}^{n} AX_i$

(b) $A \sum_{i=1}^{n} X_i = \sum_{i=1}^{n} AX_i$

(c) $A \sum_{i=1}^{n} X_i > \sum_{i=1}^{n} AX_i$

(d) Each of the above can be true in particular cases.

(b)

4.6 What is the common factor of the following expression?

$(n-1)S_1^2 + (n-1)S_2^2$. $\underline{\hspace{1cm}}$

$(n-1)$

4.7 Simplify the expression of question 4.6. $\underline{\hspace{1cm}}$

$(n-1)(S_1^2 + S_2^2)$

4.8 If we make a frequency table of many continuous measurements, the number of midpoints will usually be $\underline{\hspace{1cm}}$ [larger, smaller] than the number of measurements.

smaller

Chapter

4

Further Manipulation of Symbols and Numbers

In the first section of this chapter, a method of simplifying the operation of summation when some of the observations are alike is explained. A convenient modification of the formulas for measured variance will be discussed. In the second section, another method of simplifying computations by taking out a "common factor" is illustrated. Finally, a connection between the concept of rounding and frequency tables is explained.

A: RELATIONSHIP BETWEEN ADDITION AND MULTIPLICATION, USING FREQUENCIES

4.1 SUMMATION SIGN The summation sign Σ is frequently encountered in statistics. For example, the formula for the sample mean of n observations is

$$\bar{X} = \frac{\sum_{i=1}^{n} X_i}{n}$$

To use the formula, first sum the values of the n observations and then divide the sum by n.

- For $\sum_{i=2}^{5} X_i$, the first X_i in the sum is _____.

X_2

4.2 AVERAGE Although this formula for the sample mean is valid for any n, it is time-consuming to use for a large number of observations. For large n the computations can be shortened.

- Find the mean of each of the following three sets of numbers:

Observation	First set	Second set	Third set
X_1	3	2	3
X_2	5	2	3
X_3	0	4	3
X_4	7	4	3
X_5	5	4	3
X_6	1	4	3
X_7	8	2	3
X_8	3	2	3
	$\Sigma X_{\text{I}} =$	$\Sigma X_{\text{II}} =$	$\Sigma X_{\text{III}} =$
	$\bar{X}_{\text{I}} =$ ___	$\bar{X}_{\text{II}} =$ ___	$\bar{X}_{\text{III}} =$ ___

$\bar{X}_{\text{I}} = 4 \qquad \bar{X}_{\text{II}} = 3$
$\bar{X}_{\text{III}} = 3$

4.3 SUM OF EQUAL VALUES Perhaps you have noticed that the sum of the third set of numbers, 24, can be found by counting the number of 3's, eight of them, and multiplying $(8)(3) = 24$. This holds in general. To sum observations having the same value, we count how frequently the same value occurs. Then we multiply the frequency of occurrence by the value of the observation.

- Here is a list of observations: 56, 56, 56, 56, 56, 56, 56, 56, 56, 56. How frequently does the observation 56 occur? _____ The value of each observation is ___. Find the sum of the 10 observations. ___

10 times
56
560

4.4   symbol f   It is convenient to express this operation using symbols. Let $X_1, X_2, X_3, \ldots, X_f$ be the f observations having the same value. The letter f is used as a mnemonic device to represent frequency. If we have three observations each having the value 4, then the frequency $f = 3$, and the value $X_f = 4$.

● If we have five observations each having the value, 11, then $X_f =$ _____ and $f =$ _____.

4.5   formula for f summation   Suppose all the observations have the same value. Since the observations occur f times, the sum of these f observations is f times X_f. In symbols:

$$\sum_{i=1}^{f} X_i = fX_f$$

where all $X_i = X_f$.

● Suppose you buy 12 books costing $2.00 apiece. To find the total cost you could add $2.00 twelve times, or in symbols, letting $Y_i = \$2.00$, the total cost equals

$$\sum_{i=1}^{12} Y_i = \underline{\qquad}$$

$24.00

Alternatively, you could use the formula, total cost equals _____ $(Y_f) = \$24.00$ In general, for any number of books f, each of which costs X_f dollars, the total cost equals _____.

(12)

fX_f

4.6 f summation   Suppose you buy books which fall into three price categories. In all,

14 books cost $2.00 apiece
10 books cost $3.00 apiece
5 books cost $8.00 apiece

Let f_1 denote the number of books costing $2.00 apiece. Note that $X_{f_1} = \$2.00$. Similarly, let f_2 equal the number of books costing $3.00 apiece and f_3 the number of books costing $8.00 apiece. Then we can compute the total cost, using

$$f_1 X_{f_1} + f_2 X_{f_2} + f_3 X_{f_3} = \$98.00$$

● Compute $f_1 X_{f_1} + f_2 X_{f_2} =$ _____.

58

4.7   *f* SUMMATION   Rather than denoting the value of the first category X_{f_1}, we can just denote it X_1. This saves needless copying of the subscript *f*. The formula becomes

$$f_1X_1 + f_2X_2 + f_3X_3 = \$98.00$$

● Write the above formula, using the summation sign and subscript *i*. _____

$$\sum_{i=1}^{3} f_iX_i = \$98.00$$

4.8   *f* SUMMATION   The last problem had three categories denoting the three sets of different prices. We use the symbol *c* to denote the total number of categories of distinct sets of values. In that problem *c* = 3, and the value of the observations in the last category could be represented by X_c.

● Suppose a person has 11 pennies, 6 nickels, 2 dimes, and 4 quarters in his pocket. In this problem *c* = _____, and X_c = _____. Complete the following, using the above information.

4

quarters

$f_1 = 11$	$X_1 = \$0.01$	$f_1X_1 = \$0.11$
$f_2 =$ ____	$X_2 =$ ____	$f_2X_2 =$ ____
$f_3 =$ ____	$X_3 =$ ____	$f_3X_3 =$ ____
$f_c =$ ____	$X_c =$ ____	$f_cX_c =$ ____
		Sum: _____

6	\$0.05	\$0.30
2	0.10	0.20
4	0.25	1.00
		\$1.61

4.9   *f* SUMMATION   We can simplify the expression

$$f_1X_1 + f_2X_2 + f_3X_3 + \cdots + f_cX_c$$

by using the summation notation and writing this expression as

$$\sum_{i=1}^{c} f_iX_i$$

● The expression $\sum_{i=1}^{3} f_iX_i$ is a shorthand way of writing $f_1X_1 + f_2X_2 +$ _____.

f_3X_3

4.10 MEAN USING f Note that the total sum of any set of observations which can be grouped into categories can be found by using the expression $\sum\limits_{i=1}^{c} f_i X_i$. In symbols,

$$\sum_{i=1}^{n} X_i = \sum_{i=1}^{c} f_i X_i$$

The formula for the sample mean is

$$\overline{X} = \frac{\sum\limits_{i=1}^{n} X_i}{n}$$

Therefore an equivalent formula for the sample mean is

$$\overline{X} = \frac{\sum\limits_{i=1}^{c} f_i X_i}{n}$$

- Use both formulas to find the average cost of the following five books: $X_1 = \$2.00$, $X_2 = \$2.00$, $X_3 = \$3.00$, $X_4 = \$4.00$, and $X_5 = \$4.00$. First,

$$\sum_{i=1}^{n} X_i = 2 + 2 + 3 + 4 + 4 = \underline{\hspace{1cm}}$$ $15.00

and $$\overline{X} = \frac{\sum\limits_{i=1}^{n} X_i}{n} = \underline{\hspace{1cm}}$$ $3.00

Second,

$$\sum_{i=1}^{c} f_i X_i = (2)(2) + (3) + (\underline{\hspace{0.5cm}})(\underline{\hspace{0.5cm}}) = \$15.00$$ 2   4

and $$\overline{X} = \frac{\sum\limits_{i=1}^{c} f_i X_i}{n} = \underline{\hspace{1cm}}$$ $3.00

In the previous problem $n = \underline{\hspace{1cm}}$. Also, $f_1 = 2$, $f_2 = 1$, $f_3 = 2$.   5

$$\sum_{i=1}^{3} f_i = \underline{\hspace{1cm}}$$ 5

4.11 SUM OF f_i In general,

$$\sum_{i=1}^{c} f_i = n$$

In words, the total number of observations is always equal to the sum of the frequencies over all categories.

- If you have f_1 pennies, f_2 nickels, and f_3 dimes, then in symbols, the total number of coins, n, is

$\underline{\hspace{4cm}}$. $f_1 + f_2 + f_3 = \sum\limits_{i=1}^{3} f_i$

4.12 CALCULATING WITH f If we are taking the sum of any n numbers, some of which have the same values, we can use frequencies to simplify our computations. For example, to find the sum of the squares of the numbers 2, 2, 2, 3, and 3 we can use

$$2^2 + 2^2 + 2^2 + 3^2 + 3^2 = (3)(2^2) + (2)(3^2)$$
$$= (3)(4) + (2)(9) = 30$$

● Find the sum of the squares of the numbers 2, 2, 5, 5, 5, and 5, using frequencies. _____

$(2)(2^2) + (4)(5^2) = 108$

4.13 CALCULATING S^2 WITH f Instead of taking the sum of each X_i squared, suppose we take the sum of $(X_i - \overline{X})^2$. This quantity is needed to compute the variance, S^2. For example, if we have the following X_i: $X_1 = 1$, $X_2 = 1$, $X_3 = 1$, $X_4 = 2$, $X_5 = 2$, and $X_6 = 5$, then

$$\overline{X} = \frac{(3)(1) + (2)(2) + (1)(5)}{6} = 2$$

since we have three 1s, two 2s, and one 5. Then

$(X_1 - \overline{X}) = -1$	and	$(X_1 - \overline{X})^2 = 1$
$(X_2 - \overline{X}) = -1$		$(X_2 - \overline{X})^2 = 1$
$(X_3 - \overline{X}) = -1$		$(X_3 - \overline{X})^2 = 1$
$(X_4 - \overline{X}) = 0$		$(X_4 - \overline{X})^2 = 0$
$(X_5 - \overline{X}) = 0$		$(X_5 - \overline{X})^2 = 0$
$(X_6 - \overline{X}) = 3$		$(X_6 - \overline{X})^2 = 9$

Sum: 12

Notice that again some of the $(X_i - \overline{X})^2$ have the same value. For example, X_1 equals X_2, so $(X_1 - \overline{X})^2 = (X_2 - \overline{X})^2$. We can use the frequencies of like values to simplify our computations.

● $\displaystyle\sum_{i=1}^{6} (X_i - \overline{X})^2 = (3)(1) + (2)(0) + (1)(9) =$ ____.

12

This checks with the previous result.

4.14 CALCULATING S^2, USING f In symbols, a shorthand method for simplifying computations of S^2 is

$$\sum_{i=1}^{n} (X_i - \overline{X})^2 = \sum_{i=1}^{c} f_i(X_i - \overline{X})^2$$

where f_i denotes the frequency of the c distinct X_i values.

●) Given the X_i: 0, 2, 2, 2, 3, and 3, find $\overline{X}$ and $\displaystyle\sum_{i=1}^{c} f_i(X_i - \overline{X})^2$. First,

$$\sum_{i=1}^{3} f_i X_i = (1)(0) +\underline{\quad\quad} + \underline{\quad\quad} = 12$$

$(3)(2), (2)(3)$

$$\overline{X} = \underline{\quad}$$

2

Then

$(X_1 - \overline{X})^2 = (0-2)^2 =$ ____	and	$f_1 = 1$
$(X_2 - \overline{X})^2 = (2-2)^2 =$ ____	and	$f_2 = 3$

4

0

$(X_3 - \overline{X})^2 = (3 - 2)^2 = \underline{\quad}$ and $f_3 = \underline{\quad}$

$\sum_{i=1}^{3} f_i(X_i - \overline{X})^2 = (1)(4) + \underline{\quad} + (2)(1) = \underline{\quad}$

1   2
(3) (0)   6

4.15   VARIANCE   Because $\sum_{i=1}^{c} f_i = n$, we can write the formula for the variance S^2 either as

$$S^2 = \frac{\sum_{i=1}^{n} (X_i - \overline{X})^2}{n - 1} = \frac{\sum_{i=1}^{c} f_i(X_i - \overline{X})^2}{\sum_{i=1}^{c} f_i - 1}$$

or $$S^2 = \frac{\sum_{i=1}^{c} f_i(X_i - \overline{X})^2}{n - 1}$$

● Calculate S^2 for the problem in the previous frame.
$S^2 = \underline{\quad}$

6/5

B. COMMON FACTORS

4.16   SIMPLIFYING COMPUTATIONS   Another technique can be used which often simplifies computation. This simplification can be illustrated by the following example. Suppose we want to sum the numbers 8, 8, 8, 4, 4, 4, 1, 1, and 1. Using what we learned in Section A, we can write the sum as

Sum $= (3)(8) + (3)(4) + (3)(1) = 39$

Alternatively, because it makes *no* difference in what order we add numbers, we could add the original numbers as follows:

$8 + 4 + 1 + 8 + 4 + 1 + 8 + 4 + 1 = 39$

Note that we can consider $8 + 4 + 1$ as a single number which occurs with a frequency of 3, so using the techniques of Section A, we have

Sum $= 3(8 + 4 + 1) = (3)(13) = 39$

Comparing the above results, we see

$(3)(8 + 4 + 1) = (3)(8) + (3)(4) + (3)(1)$

● $(2)(4) + (2)(6) + (2)(10) = \underline{\quad} (4 + 6 + 10)$
  $(2)(4 + 6 + 10) = \underline{\quad}$
  $(2)(4) + (2)(6) + (2)(10) = \underline{\quad}$

2
40
40

4.17   ORDER OF COMPUTATIONS   Suppose we know the heights of five men. Let $X_1 = 70$ inches, $X_2 = 71$ inches, $X_3 = 69$ inches, $X_4 = 72$ inches, and $X_5 = 68$ inches. Suppose we wish to find the mean height in centimeters, noting that 1 inch = 2.54 centimeters. There are two methods of calculating the mean height in centimeters. First, we can convert each man's height to centimeters. To do this we would multiply (2.54) times each X_i separately, obtaining

$$(2.54)X_1 + (2.54)X_2 + (2.54)X_3 + (2.54)X_4 + (2.54)X_5$$
$$= \text{sum in centimeters}$$

Instead of performing five multiplications, we can simplify the computation by finding the total of the heights in inches first and then multiplying this total by 2.54.

- Sum in centimeters $= (2.54)(X_1 + X_2 + X_3 + X_4 + X_5)$. Choose the easier way of finding the total height in centimeters and compute it.

Sum in centimeters = _____   889 cm

Find the average height rounded to whole centimeters:

$$\overline{X} = \text{_____}$$ 178 cm

4.18 ORDER OF COMPUTATIONS Using the summation sign, we can simplify the formulas in the previous frame. For example,

$$\sum_{i=1}^{5} X_i = X_1 + X_2 + X_3 + X_4 + X_5$$

and $$\sum_{i=1}^{5} aX_i = aX_1 + aX_2 + aX_3 + aX_4 + aX_5$$

In the preceding problem $a = 2.54$ centimeters. Before, it was shown that

$$(2.54)(X_1 + X_2 + X_3 + X_4 + X_5) = 2.54X_1$$
$$+ 2.54X_2 + 2.54X_3 + 2.54X_4 + 2.54X_5$$

In symbols this would be

$$2.54 \sum_{i=1}^{5} X_i = \sum_{i=1}^{5} 2.54X_i$$

or in general,

$$a \sum_{i=1}^{n} X_i = \sum_{i=1}^{n} aX_i$$

- In using the expression, $\sum_{i=1}^{n} aX_i$, do we perform the operation of addition or multiplication first? _____ In the preceding problem, how   multiplication
many multiplications do you perform? _____ If you n
use the expression $a \sum_{i=1}^{n} X_i$, how many multiplications
do you perform? _____   1

4.19 COMMON FACTOR In the previous example, the list of measurements (70 inches, 71 inches, 69 inches, 72 inches, and 68 inches) was equivalent to 178 cm, 180 cm, 175 cm, 183 cm, and 173 cm, or to 2.54 times the height in inches. The number 2.54 can be referred to as a "common factor" of the set of measurements in centimeters.

- If we consider the relationship of inches to feet, the "common factor" is _____.

4.20 COMMON FACTOR In symbols, if we have the measurement aX_1, aX_2, and aX_3, then "a" is a "common factor" of these three measurements. Using the previous results, we obtain

$$\sum_{i=1}^{3} aX_i = a \sum_{i=1}^{3} X_i$$

- The sum of a "common factor" times each X_i is equal to the _____ times the _____ of the X_i. Which symbol is the "common factor" in the following expressions?

	common factor sum
$\sum_{i=1}^{n} a^2(X_i - \bar{X})^2$ _____	a^2
$\sum_{i=1}^{k} S^2(1/n_i)^2$ _____	S^2
$\sum_{i=1}^{2} (n-1)S_i^2$ _____	$n-1$
$S^2(1/n_1) + S^2(1/n_2)$ _____	S^2
$\sigma^2(1/n_1) + \sigma^2(1/n_2)$ _____	σ^2
$\dfrac{\sigma^2}{n_1} + \dfrac{\sigma^2}{n_2}$ _____	σ^2
$(n-1)S_1^2 + (n-1)S_2^2$ _____	$(n-1)$

C: CONCEPTS BASIC TO FREQUENCY TABLES

4.21 DISCRETE MEASUREMENTS The number of coins is a discrete measurement. To calculate the sum of discrete measurements, we can count the frequency of occurrence of each distinct number directly. For example, we can count the num-

ber of nickels and multiply by 5 cents to obtain the sum of
the value of the nickels.

- Measurements for which fractions have no meaning are
called discrete measurements. List A is composed of
discrete measurements. List B contains continuous
measurements rounded off to the nearest hundredth.

A: 2   2   2   2   3   3   4   4
B: 2.16 2.84 2.71 2.34 3.01 3.25 4.09 4.65

How many distinct numbers occur in List A? _____   3
How many distinct numbers occur in List B? _____   8
If $X_1 = 2$ in List A, what is f_1? _____   If $X_1 = 2.16$ 4
in List B, what is f_1? _____   Does it save any time to   1

use $\sum_{i=1}^{c} f_i X_i$ rather than $\sum_{i=1}^{n} X_i$ if all the $f_i = 1$?

_____ If all the $f_i = 1$, then n _____ c.   no   equals
Note that it does not save time to use the frequency
formula unless n is large.

4.22 DISTINCT VALUES Notice that as we round off the values of each observation, fewer distinct values will occur.

- Given 2.16, 2.84, 2.78, 2.34, 3.01, 3.28, and 3.33, how
many distinct values are there? _____   Round off these   7
numbers to the nearest tenth. For example, 2.16 can
be rounded off to 2.2. The remaining values are

_____   _____   _____   2.8 2.8 2.3
_____   _____   _____   3.0 3.3 3.3

How many distinct values are there among these numbers? _____   Round off these numbers to the nearest   5
whole number.

_____   _____   _____   2 3 3
_____   _____   _____   2 3 3
_____   3

How many distinct values are there among these
numbers? _____   2

4.23 ONE NUMBER TO REPRESENT MANY When we round
off a number, we use one number to represent many numbers.
For example, in the previous problem, by rounding off 2.84,
2.78, 3.01, 3.28, and 3.33 to 3, we have changed five distinct
numbers to one number.

- Round off the following numbers so they can be represented by one single digit number. 4.1, 3.9, and 4.2
can be rounded off to _____.   4

4.24   USE OF MIDPOINT   This is somewhat similar to what we do in a frequency table. In a frequency table we use the mid-point of a class interval to represent all the X_i values in an interval. In a frequency table we use one number, the mid-point, to represent many numbers.

●   If you have a frequency table with three class intervals, how many distinct X_i values will you use? _____   3

Review: Chapter 4

4.1   Suppose the following postage stamps are purchased: 10 one-cent, 15 five-cent, and 8 ten-cent stamps. For this problem what numbers correspond to:

$$n \text{ _____} \qquad f_1 \text{ _____}$$

$$c \text{ _____} \qquad X_2 \text{ _____}$$

$$\sum_{i=1}^{c} f_i X_i = \text{_____}$$

33   10

3   5¢

$1.65

4.2   A farmer owns ten fields, three of which are 100 yards long, five of which are 110 yards long and two of which are 75 yards long. If all fields are square in shape, how much land does the farmer own? _____

101,750 sq yd

4.3   Compute the variance of the numbers 1, 1, 1, 1, 1, 7, using the formula

$$S^2 = \frac{\sum\limits_{i=1}^{c} f_i (X_i - \overline{X})^2}{n-1} \quad \text{_____}$$

$S^2 = 6$

4.4   What are the common factors of the following expressions?

$5(7) + 5(8) + 5(9)$ _____	5
$6(17) + 6(17) + 7(17)$ _____	17
$nx_1 + nx_2 + nx_3$ _____	n
$\sum\limits_{i=1}^{n} aX_i$ _____	a
$\dfrac{\sigma^2}{n_1} + \dfrac{\sigma^2}{n_2}$ _____	σ^2

4.5   Compute, using common factors:

$$4(9) + 4(1) + 6(3) + 6(2) + 6(5) = \text{_____}$$

100

4.6   In a frequency table, we use a midpoint to represent each of the observations in the _____ _____ .

class interval

Preview Questions: Chapter 5

5.1   Solve the equation $(X - \mu)/\sigma = Z$ for X. $X = $ _____

$$Z\sigma + \mu$$

5.2   If

$$\frac{\sum\limits_{i=1}^{n} X_i}{n} = \bar{X}$$

then $\sum\limits_{i=1}^{n} X_i = $ _____?

$$n\bar{X}$$

5.3   Solve the equation $(\bar{X} - \mu)/(\sigma/\sqrt{n}) = Z$ for $\sqrt{n}$. $\sqrt{n} = $ _____

$$Z\sigma/(\bar{X} - \mu)$$

5.4   True or False: In solving both the equation $5 + Z = 8$ and the equation $Z + 7 = 2$, the first step involves the operation opposite to addition. _____

true

5.5   True or False: When eliminating terms from the side of an equation which contains an unknown, addition or subtraction should be considered before multiplication or division, unless otherwise stated by means of parentheses. _____

true

5.6   True or False: When performing arithmetical calculations in which the order of operations is unspecified, the order in which operations are performed is the opposite of the order of operations considered in equation solving. _____

true

5.7   Solve these equations:
$$(3X - 1)9 + 2 = 20 \qquad X = \text{\_\_\_\_}$$
$$(3X + 2)9 = 20 \qquad X = \text{_____}$$

1

2/27

Chapter 5

The Algebraic Essentials of Elementary Statistics

This chapter reviews the basic tools of algebra, which will help you in working with statistical formulas. Although there are many different formulas used in elementary statistics, most are variations of a few basic ones. Knowledge of only a few rules of algebra will enable you to manipulate the basic statistical formulas into their most convenient form. In the first section, some rules for working with equations are given. In the second section, the order of operations in solving equations is discussed.

A: GOLDEN RULE OF EQUATIONS

5.1   DEFINITION OF EQUATION   In the first section of Chapter 3, "Manipulating Symbols and Numbers," an equation was defined as a symbolic way of writing a sentence in which the main verb is "equals."

- If a shoe manufacturer produces X right shoes and Y left shoes (the same number of both types of shoes is produced), express the relationship between the two types of shoes in symbols. _____ Is this relationship an equation? _____

$X = Y$

yes

5.2   GOLDEN RULE OF EQUATIONS   The golden rule is
   Do unto one side what you do unto the other

- If the manufacturer decides to produce 50 more left shoes, how many more right shoes must he produce to preserve the equality? _____ In symbols,

$$Y + 50 = X + \underline{\quad}$$

50

50

5.3   GOLDEN RULE OF EQUATIONS   In the previous problem, the golden rule of equations was followed, since we added 50 to both sides of the equation. If we subtracted 50 from one side of the equation, then to preserve the equality we would have to subtract 50 from the other side of the equation.

- If $X = Y$, then $50X = \underline{\quad} Y$.

50

5.4   GOLDEN RULE OF EQUATIONS   Also, if we divide one side of an equation by a number, we must divide the other side by the same number to preserve the equality. For example, we know $(3)(5 + 1) = 18$. Dividing both sides by 2 preserves the equality,

$$\frac{(3)(5 + 1)}{2} = \frac{18}{2}$$

which equals 9.

- If $a(b + c) = d$, then $\dfrac{a(b + c)}{e} = \dfrac{d}{?}$.

e

5.5   GOLDEN RULE OF EQUATIONS   It is important to be able to "solve" equations. An equation is usually composed of several symbols. To solve an equation for one particular symbol we must manipulate the equation, using the golden rule so that the desired symbol appears alone on the left-hand side of the equation. For example, if X is the desired symbol and we have $X + 1 = 3$, then if we subtract 1 from both sides of the equation, we have

$$X + 1 - 1 = 3 - 1 \quad \text{or} \quad X = 2$$

and we have solved the equation for X.

●   In symbols, if we have $X + A = B$, then to solve the equation for X we will subtract A from both sides of the equation.

$$X + A - A = B - A$$
$$A - A = \underline{\hspace{2cm}}$$
$$X + 0 = \underline{\hspace{1cm}}$$

The solved equation is $\underline{\hspace{4cm}}$.

zero

X

$X = B - A$

5.6   SOLVING EQUATIONS   Let's try solving another equation. To solve the equation $2X = 4$, we will divide both sides of the equation by 2, obtaining

$$\frac{2X}{2} = \frac{4}{2}$$

Since $2/2 = 1$ and $1X = X$, we have solved the equation and can write the results as

$$X = \frac{4}{2} \quad \text{or} \quad X = 2$$

●   In words, if two times an unknown number of books is four, then the number of books is $\underline{\hspace{2cm}}$.

two

5.7   SOLVING EQUATIONS   Notice that if the symbol we wish to isolate on the left-hand side of the equation has a number added to it, we must subtract this number from both sides of the equation. For example, with $X + 1 = 3$, we subtracted 1 from both sides of the equation, obtaining $X = 2$.

●   If there is any number, B, added to the symbol we wish to solve for, X, then the solution is obtained by $\underline{\hspace{3cm}}$ B from both sides of the equation.

subtracting

5.8   OPPOSITE OPERATIONS   Subtraction can be considered as the opposite of addition, and division as the opposite of multiplication. To solve an equation we must perform a series of operations which are opposite to the operations appearing on the left-hand side of the equation. For example, if

$X + 2 = 4$, then to solve for X we note that 2 is added to X, so we perform the opposite operation and subtract 2.

- If $3X = 6$, then to remove the 3 which multiplies X, we must _____ both sides of the equation by 3. Division is the operation opposite to but paired with _____. Given $2\sigma = 5$, then $\sigma =$ ___. Given $\sigma/2 = 5$, then $\sigma =$ ___. Given

$$\frac{\sum\limits_{i=1}^{n} X_i}{n} = \overline{X}$$

then

$$\sum\limits_{i=1}^{n} X_i = \underline{\hspace{2cm}}$$

divide

multiplication   5/2
10

$(n)\,(\overline{X})$

5.9   SOLVING A STATISTICAL EQUATION   We frequently work with the following equation in statistics:

$$\frac{X - \mu}{\sigma} = Z$$

Suppose we want to solve for X. The first step is to remove the σ from the left-hand side of the equation. Since $X - \mu$ is divided by σ, we multiply both sides by σ, obtaining $X - \mu = (\sigma)\,(Z)$ or, removing parentheses, $X - \mu = \sigma Z$. Now to remove the μ which is subtracted from X, we add μ to both sides of the equation, obtaining

$$X = \mu + \sigma Z$$

- We can check our results, using actual numbers. If $X = 18$, $\mu = 6$, and $\sigma = 4$, then, using the formula $Z = (X - \mu)/\sigma$, compute $Z =$ ___. Compute $\mu + \sigma Z =$ ___, using the above numbers. In the numerical example, does $X = \mu + \sigma Z$? _____

3
18
yes, $18 = 18$

5.10   STEPS IN SOLVING EQUATIONS   The solution of an equation, like the solution of a puzzle, sometimes requires several steps. The first step is to arrange the equation so that the unknown is on the left-hand side. Suppose we wish to solve the following equation for σ:

$$2 = \frac{S}{\sigma}$$

To arrange the equation so that we can solve for σ, we multiply both sides of the equation by σ, obtaining

$$2\sigma = S$$

Now, σ is on the left-hand side. Since the σ is multiplied by 2, we *divide* both sides of the equation by 2 (the opposite operation), obtaining

$$\sigma = \frac{S}{2}$$

- Given $Z = (X - \mu)/\sigma$, solve for σ.

  $\sigma =$ _____

$$\sigma = \frac{X - \mu}{Z}$$

5.11 STEPS IN SOLVING EQUATIONS In the following equation treat $\sqrt{n}$ as a single symbol.

$$\frac{\overline{X} - \mu}{\sigma/\sqrt{n}} = Z$$

Suppose we wish to solve for $\sqrt{n}$. First, we multiply both sides by $\sigma/\sqrt{n}$ to remove this expression from the denominator, obtaining

$$X - \mu = (Z)\frac{\sigma}{\sqrt{n}}$$

Now, multiplying both sides by the $\sqrt{n}$ will remove $\sqrt{n}$ from the denominator of the right-hand side and place it on the left-hand side:

$$\sqrt{n}\,(\overline{X} - \mu) = (Z)\,(\sigma)$$

Since $\sqrt{n}$ is multiplied by $\overline{X} - \mu$, removing $\overline{X} - \mu$ from the left-hand side, we obtain the answer:

$$\sqrt{n} = \frac{(Z)\,(\sigma)}{\overline{X} - \mu}$$

- Given $1/\sqrt{n} = 1/4$, solve for $\sqrt{n}$. $\sqrt{n} = $ _____.

$\sqrt{n} = 4$

5.12 RELATIONSHIP BETWEEN A NUMERATOR AND A DENOMINATOR When we have an expression such as $(X - \mu)$ which is divided by a symbol such as σ, we can consider the expression to be multiplied by the reciprocal of the symbol (or $1/\sigma$). That is,

$$\frac{X - \mu}{\sigma} = (X - \mu)\frac{1}{\sigma}$$

This holds true for any fraction. Fractions can always be expressed as the product of the numerator times one over the denominator (reciprocal of the denominator).

- $6/3 = (6)\,(\underline{\quad})$. What is the common factor in

$$\frac{\sigma_1}{n} + \frac{\sigma_2}{n} \quad \underline{\quad}$$

$1/3$

$1/n$

B: DECIDING HOW TO SOLVE AN EQUATION

5.13 SOLVING EQUATIONS In the previous section we first stated the basic golden rule for solving equations: Do unto one side what you do unto the other. We then answered the question: "Do *what* to both sides?" The answer was this: "Perform the operation opposite to the operation which links the symbol we wish to remove to the symbol we wish to solve for."

- To solve the equation $X + 3 = 10$, we *subtract* 3 from both sides of the equation because the operation which links the X and the 3 is _____.

addition

5.14 ORDER OF OPERATIONS When the solution to an equation requires several steps, we must take the steps in the correct order. For example, to solve $(X - \mu)/\sigma = Z$ for X we first multiplied both sides of the equation by σ and then added μ to both sides of the result. For example,

Step 1: $$\frac{X - \mu}{\sigma} \sigma = Z(\sigma)$$

or $$X - \mu = Z\sigma$$

Step 2: $$X - \mu + \mu = Z\sigma + \mu$$

or $$X = Z\sigma + \mu$$

● In the example above, the order of operations performed is multiplication followed by _____.

addition

5.15 ORDER OF OPERATIONS The two operations which appear in the equation, $(X - \mu)/\sigma = Z$, are subtraction and division. This indicates that we must both add and multiply to solve the equation. The characteristic which distinguishes between the two operations in this case is that one operation takes place within the parentheses, while the other occurs outside the parentheses.

● To solve $(X - \mu)/\sigma = Z$ for the unknown X, which operation (addition or multiplication) do we apply first? _____ The operation of division occurs _____ [outside or inside] the parentheses?

multiplication
outside

5.16 ORDER OF OPERATIONS The previous frame illustrates an important principle of the solution of equations. Since an expression enclosed within parentheses is a single entity with respect to operations outside it, the outside terms should be removed first. Then the operations within the parentheses are considered.

● In the equation $(X + 3)5 = 10$ we must first _____ each side of the equation by 5 since 5 occurs outside the parentheses.

divide

5.17 ORDER OF OPERATIONS The rule we are discussing can be applied several times in the process of solving an equation. Consider the equation

$$(3(X + 3))/5 = 6$$

There are two sets of parentheses.

● The operation of _____ appears outside both sets of parentheses. Therefore we first multiply both sides of the equation by _____.

division

5

5.18 ORDER OF OPERATIONS The first step of the solution of $(3(X+3))/5 = 6$ changed the equation to $(3(X+3)) = 30$. There is no need to include parentheses to enclose an entire side of an equation, and so the equation can be written without the outer set of parentheses as $3(X+3) = 30$.

- The operation which now appears outside the equation and links the 3 to the $(X+3)$ is _____.   multiplication
  Therefore we must _____ both sides of the equa-   divide
  tion by 3. As a result we obtain $(X+3) = 10$, which
  can be written without the parentheses as $X + 3 = 10$.
  What is X? _____   7

5.19 ORDER OF OPERATIONS In the second section of Chapter 3 we learned that parentheses are used to specify the order of operations. If an equation contains two or more operations on the same side as the unknown and yet does not specify the order of operation with parentheses, it is important to choose the correct sequence of steps to solve the equation.

- In the equation $3Z + 5 = 10$ there are no parentheses and yet there are _____ operations which appear   two
  on the side of the equation which contains the unknown Z.

5.20 ORDER OF OPERATIONS In the equation $3Z + 5 = 10$ we must eliminate the $+5$ first and then remove the 3 which multiplies the Z.

- Solve for Z: $3Z + 5 = 10$ _____ $Z = 5/3$
  Solve for X: $7 + 10X = 10$ _____ $X = 3/10$

5.21 ORDER OF OPERATIONS In the equation $5 + Z/3 = 10$ we would again eliminate the 5 first and then remove the 3.

- To solve $5 + Z/3 = 10$, first subtract 5 from both sides of the equation; this leaves $Z/3 = 5$; $Z = $ _____.   15

5.22 RULE FOR ORDER OF OPERATIONS A general rule for ordering the steps to solve equations where the order is not specified by parentheses is this: "*Addition* or *subtraction* must *precede multiplication* or *division*."

- To solve the equations

$$3Z + 5 = 10$$
$$7 + 10X = 10$$
$$5 + Z/3 = 10$$

we first _____ a number from each side. To solve   subtract
the equation $3Z - 5 = 10$, we first _____ a num-   add
ber to each side.

5.23   RULE FOR ORDER OF OPERATIONS   As a mnemonic device, one can remember that the operations should be considered in the same order in which these operations were learned.   The addition and subtraction of numbers is learned several grades before multiplication and division.   This mnemonic device is applicable not only to addition, subtraction, multiplication, and division, but also to the still more complex operations of exponentiation and extracting roots.   For example, to solve $3X^2 + 9 = 16$ one would first subtract 9, then divide by 3, and finally take the square root of both sides of the equation.

- If $2X^2 - 12 = 6$, then $X =$ _____.

  If $(3Y - 1)9 = 18$, then $Y =$ _____.

3 (or -3)

1

5.24   EQUATION SOLUTION VERSUS ARITHMETIC COMPUTATION The solution of an equation can be defined as the *elimination* of all terms except the unknown from one side of the equation. In this case we first consider addition or subtraction and then consider multiplication or division.   An arithmetic computation, on the other hand, can be defined as the *combination* of numbers into a single number.   From this point of view, equation solution and arithmetic computation are opposite procedures.   Notice that when solving an equation we consider addition or subtraction before multiplication or division.   Conversely, in arithmetic computation we multiply or divide before we add or subtract.   For example, to compute $10(2) + 3$ we first multiply 10 times 2 and then add 3.   To solve $10X+3=23$ we first consider the $+ 3$ and *then* the 10 which multiplies X.

- To solve the equation $3X - 4 = 2$, we first consider the _____ and then the _____ which multiplies X.   To compute $3(2) - 4$, we first consider the _____ which multiplies 2 and then the _____.

-4 3

3

-4

5.25   EQUATION SOLUTION   The formula $X = \mu + \sigma Z$ is frequently encountered in statistics.   Suppose one wishes to solve this equation for Z.   The Z is multiplied by σ, and the μ is added to this product.

- Which symbol should be removed first?   _____.   In other words, $\sigma Z = X$ _____ and $Z = (X - \mu)/($_____$)$

μ

$-\mu$ σ

5.26   USING PARENTHESES   Notice that we must use parentheses to enclose $(X - \mu)$.

- Where $X = 2$, $\mu = 1$, and $\sigma = 2$, compute

$$(X - \mu)/\sigma \qquad \text{\_\_\_\_\_}$$

$$X - \mu/\sigma \qquad \text{\_\_\_\_\_}$$

1/2

3/2

5.27 USING PARENTHESES To compute $X - \mu/\sigma$ we first divide μ by σ and then subtract the result from X. It is very important to notice that $(X - \mu)/\sigma$ is not in general equal to $X - \mu/\sigma$.

● Is $(X + 4)/6 = X + 4/6$? _____

no

5.28 USING PARENTHESES We can avoid a very common mistake by using parentheses. To solve $X - \mu = \sigma Z$ for Z, we should enclose $X - \mu$ in parentheses. Thus $Z = (X - \mu)/\sigma$. When one multiplies or divides a side of an equation by a number or symbol, the *whole* side must be multiplied or divided. If we multiply or divide both sides of an equation by a number or symbol we should use parentheses to group terms before the operation is performed.

● Divide both sides of the following equation by 2:
$2 = X + Y + 6$ _____

$1 = (X + Y + 6)/2$

5.29 REVIEW The golden rule of solving equations is to do unto one side what you do unto the other. The solution to an equation is obtained when the unknown is alone on the left-hand side of the equation. We perform the operations of addition or subtraction before multiplication or division. The operation we perform is always opposite to the operation linking the symbols. Arithmetic computations are unlike equation solving. We consider multiplication or division before addition or subtraction.

Review: Chapter 5

5.1 Solve the following equations:

$1 + X = 6$	$X = $ _____	5
$2X + 3 = 4$	$X = $ _____	$1/2$
$S/\sigma = 5$	$S = $ _____	5σ
$S/\sigma = 10$	$\sigma = $ _____	$S/10$
$(X + 2)3 = 6$	$X = $ _____	0
$(X + 2)/3 = 6$	$X = $ _____	16
$(X + 2)3 - 4 = 8$	$X = $ _____	2
$\dfrac{X - \mu}{\sigma} = Z$	$X = $ _____	$\mu + \sigma Z$
$M\dfrac{(X - \mu)}{\sigma} = Z$	$X = $ _____	$\mu + \sigma Z/M$
$2((X + 1)3 - 2) = 8$	$X = $ _____	1

5.2   When numbers 2, 8, and 3, which appear in the expression $2(8) + 3$, are *combined*, the operation of _____ precedes the operation of _____.

multiplication
addition

5.3   When the numbers 2 and 3 are eliminated from the left-hand side of the equation $2X + 3 = 19$, we perform the operation of _____ before the operation of _____.

subtraction
division

5.4   When the numbers 9, 16, and 2 which appear in the expression $2(9 + 16)$ are to be combined, the operation of _____ precedes the operation of _____.

addition   multiplication

5.5   When the numbers 2 and 9 are removed from the left-hand side of the equation $2(9 + X) = 50$, the operation of _____ is considered before the operation of _____.

division
subtraction

5.6   Write the following equation in symbols: X plus 15 quantity squared equals 30. _____

$(X + 15)^2 = 30$

5.7   If both the operations of addition and multiplication appear on the side of an *equation* which contains the unknown, then the operation of division is performed first if the plus sign appears within the _____.

parentheses

5.8   In numerical computations, the order of operations is _____ to that of solving equations.

opposite

5.9   The four operations which we have been considering can be grouped into pairs. Which pair is usually learned first? _____ _____

addition   subtraction

5.10   To solve the equation $6X + 3 = 12$, we perform first the operation which was learned _____.

first

5.11   The following consists of two equations and two computations:

$$6X - 3 = 9 \qquad 6(X - 3) = 9 \qquad 6(2) - 3 \qquad 6(9 - 3)$$

In which equation and in which computation is subtraction considered first? _____ _____

$6X - 3 = 9$ $6(9 - 3)$

Preview Questions: Chapter 6

6.1 Which of the following equations is always valid and which invalid?

 (*a*) $(X_i - \bar{X})^2 = (\bar{X} - X_i)^2$ ———————   valid

 (*b*) $2(X_i - \bar{X}) = 2(\bar{X} - X_i)$ ———————   invalid

 (*c*) $X_i - \bar{X} + 2 = \bar{X} - X_i + 2$ ———————   invalid

6.2 Is the answer to $(-14)(-2)(8)(-18)(-0.5)$ positive or negative? ———————   positive

6.3 True or False: $(287)(-17)$ is not equal to $(287)(17)$, but $(287)(-17)(-17)$ is equal to $(287)(17)(17)$. ———————   true

6.4 True or False: If $A = B$, then $-A = -B$. ———————   true

6.5 True or False: If $A < B$, then $-A < -B$. ———————   false

6.6 True or False: If $A < B$, then $1/A < 1/B$. ———————   false

6.7 Find an inequality with only X on the left-hand side if $-2X < 8$. ——————— $X > -4$

6.8 Find an inequality with only X on the left-hand side if $X/(-2) < 8$. ——————— $X > -16$

6.9 If $S/\sigma < 5$, then is $\sigma/S < 1/5$? ———————   no

Chapter 6

Picturing Equalities and Inequalities

Although the rules of algebra are considered by some people to be equivalent to the rules of a game — to be followed but not interpreted or understood — this approach has at least one major drawback. Knowledge of algebra obtained in this way is difficult to apply to actual problems, particularly those arising in statistics.

In this chapter several rules of algebra, specifically rules concerning properties of inequalities and properties of the number -1, will be considered pictorially. In the first section, we discuss how to work with negative numbers. In the second section, inequalities are defined and rules for working with them are outlined. Study of these sections will lead to added understanding of statistical formulas and reduce the need for rote memorization.

A: PROPERTIES OF NEGATIVE NUMBERS

6.1   POSITIVE AND NEGATIVE NUMBERS   We previously used
the thermometer scale to describe positive and negative numbers. Rather than draw a thermometer in each of the following examples, we will draw a line and place the numbers on
the line as follows:

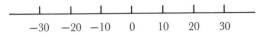

● If X is a negative number, which side of zero is it on?
_____ [left or right]

left

6.2   REPRESENTATION OF INEQUALITIES   If X and Y are two
numbers, and X is less than Y $(X < Y)$, then X is to the left
of Y on the scale.

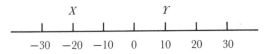

● If W and Z are two numbers, and W is greater than
Z $(W > Z)$, then W is to the _____ of Z on the
scale.

right

6.3   SYMMETRY ABOUT ZERO   Notice that positive and negative numbers are symmetric about zero. For instance, $+10$
is ten units to the right of zero and -10 is ten units to the
left of zero.
● What number is halfway between $+20$ and -20?
_____

zero

6.4   ROTATION   Let us assume that our number scale is fixed.
Let us consider the point zero and an arbitrary point, say
$X = 21$ cm. To keep the distance between 0 and 21 cm constant we could stretch a piece of taut string between them.

Holding the string at zero we could rotate the free end of the string until it again reached the other side of the scale.

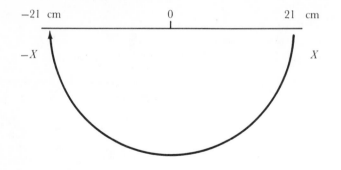

- Where will the free end of the taut string intercept the scale? _____

6.5   ROTATION   A symbolic way of expressing the operation of a half-turn rotation is multiplication by minus one. Thus minus one times X equals minus X, or in symbols, $(-1)X = -X$.

- $(-1)(0.05) = $ _____.

6.6   ROTATION   Multiplying a number by (-1) rotates it a half-turn around the zero point. We can rotate it a full-turn by multiplying it by (-1) twice. This brings the point back to its original position.

- $(-1)(-1)X = (-1)(-X) = X.$ $(-1)(-1)(25) = $ _____

6.7   IDENTITY CONCEPT   If we multiply any number by 1, it remains unchanged. Since multiplying a number twice by minus one leaves the number unchanged, $(-1)(-1)$ is equal to 1. Writing this as an equation, we have $(-1)(-1) = 1$ or $(-1)(-1) X = 1X = X$.

- $(-1)(-1)(5) = $ _____. $(-1)(-1)(-5) = $ _____.

6.8   ORDER OF MULTIPLICATION   You know that $(6)(5) = (5)(6) = 30$. If you multiply two numbers, the order of multiplication does not affect the answer. This holds true for any number of numbers regardless of whether they are positive or negative.

- Figure *a* shows three connected sticks each of which is two centimeters long. Figure *b* shows two connected sticks each of which is three centimeters long.

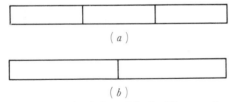

(*a*)

(*b*)

The total length of the sticks in Figure *a* is equal to the total length of the sticks in Figure *b*. This illustrates that

$$(3)(2) = \underline{\hspace{2cm}} = 6$$

(2) (3)

Without doing any computation, decide which of the following pairs of products are equal. List (by letter) the pairs which are equalities.

A $(256)(-1)(54)$ and $(-1)(54)(256)$
B $(256)(-1)(54)$ and $(1)(54)(256)$
C $(10)(-1)(-1)(136)$ and $(-1)(-1)(10)(136)$
D $(3)(X)$ and $(X)(3)$
E $(X)(Y)(Z)$ and $(Y)(Z)(X)$

A, C, D, E

6.9 MULTIPLICATION OF NEGATIVES We can write -256 as $(-1)(256)$ and (-10) as $(-1)(10)$. Therefore, if we want to multiply (-256) by (-10), the result is equal to $(-1)(256)(-1)(10)$, or $(-1)(-1)(10)(256)$, or $(1)(10)(256)$, or simply $(10)(256)$, which equals 2,560. The product of any two negative numbers is a positive number. If we multiply any number by (-1) times (-1), the first (-1) rotates the number a half turn. The second multiplication rotates the number back to its original position.

- If you multiply (-18) times (-5) you can write this as $(-1)(-1)$ times $\underline{\hspace{2cm}}$ or 90. We have performed the equivalent of rotating 90 by $\underline{\hspace{2cm}}$ half turns.

(18) (5)
two

6.10 MULTIPLICATION OF NEGATIVES A shorthand way of writing $(5)(5)$ is 5^2 or $(X)(X) = X^2$. We know that $(-1)(-1) = 1$, since this involves a full-turn rotation. Thus $(-1)(-1) = (-1)^2 = 1$. But $(1)^2 = 1$ so that $(-1)^2 = (1)^2$. This is true for all numbers. The square of a negative number equals the square of the positive value of the same number. For example, $(-256)^2 = (256)^2$.

- $(-1,029)^2 = ($ _____ $)^2$. Because squaring a negative number is equivalent to multiplying two numbers together, and because the product of two negative numbers is positive, the square of a negative number must be _____. In the formula for the variance,

$$S^2 = \frac{\sum_{i=1}^{n} (X_i - \bar{X})^2}{n - 1}$$

Every $(X_i - \bar{X})^2$ is _____.

1,029

positive

positive

B: MANIPULATING INEQUALITIES

6.11 INEQUALITIES On the following scale a point at 10 is to the left of 20 (10 is less than 20 or, in symbols, $10 < 20$), and a point at 20 is to the left of 25 ($20 < 25$).

```
•    •    •    •    •    •    •    •    •    •    •
0    5   10   15   20   25   30   35   40   45   50
```

- On the following scale a point at -20 is to the _____ of -10.

left

```
 •    •    •    •    •    •    •    •    •    •    •
-20  -10   0   10   20   30   40   50   60   70   80
```

In symbols, this means -20 _____ -10.

<

6.12 INEQUALITIES Notice that $-20 < -10$ and yet that $20 > 10$. Before, when we changed a plus to a minus sign, we represented this by rotating a taut string a half turn. We can think of changing the inequality between 10 and 20 by rotation:

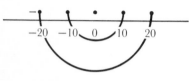

Notice that 20 is to the right of 10 and -20 to the left of -10. In symbols,

$$20 > 10$$
$$-20 < -10$$

- 20°F is warmer than 10°F, and $-20°$F is _____ than $-10°$F.

colder

6.13 RULE FOR INEQUALITIES, POSITIVE NUMBERS   The golden rule for equations is to do unto one side what you do unto the other. For inequalities, the situation is a little more complicated. The rule for inequalities is this: "Add or subtract any number from both sides of the inequality, and multiply or divide by any *positive* number without changing the inequality sign."

- You know that $5 > 4$. Compute $5 + 2$ and $4 + 2$, and check whether $5 + 2 > 4 + 2$. _____   yes $(7 > 6)$
  Given $5 > 4$. Compute $(2)(5)$ and $(2)(4)$ and check whether $(2)(5) > (2)(4)$. _____   yes $(10 > 8)$
  Given $5 > 4$. Compute $5 - 10$ and $4 - 10$ and check whether $5 - 10 > 4 - 10$. _____   yes $(-5 > -6)$

6.14 RULE FOR INEQUALITIES, NEGATIVE NUMBERS   The rule for multiplying or dividing an inequality by a negative number is that you multiply or divide both sides of the inequality and change the direction of the inequality. For example,

$$10 > 8$$
then
$$(-1)(10) < (-1)(8)$$
or
$$-10 < -8$$

- Given $3 > -3$, multiply both sides of the inequality by (-1) to obtain $(-1)(3) < (-1)(-3)$ or _____. $-3 < 3$
  Given $10 > 5$, multiply both sides of the inequality by (-2) to obtain _____. Given $10 > 5$, divide both $-20 < -10$
  sides of the inequality by (-5) to obtain _____. $-2 < -1$
  Given $X < Y$, multiply both sides of the inequality by (-1), obtaining _____. $-X > -Y$

6.15 FRACTIONS   So far we have worked only with whole numbers. In statistics we will use numbers which are fractions such as $3/5$ or $9/10$. A fraction is composed of two parts. The part above (or to the left of) the division bar is called a numerator, and the part below (or to the right of) the division bar is called a denominator. For the fraction $3/5$, 3 is the numerator and 5 is the denominator.

- For the fraction $9/10$, 9 is the _____   numerator
  and 10 is the _____.   denominator

6.16 FRACTIONS   Many statistical expressions are in the form of fractions. For example, S^2 is the numerator and n is the denominator in the expression S^2/n.

- In the fraction S^2/σ^2, σ^2 is the _____   denominator
  and S^2 is the _____.   numerator

6.17   FRACTIONS   Whole numbers can be written as fractions. Suppose we have the number 5. We can write this as the fraction 5/1 because 5 divided by 1 equals 5.

●   6/1 = _____.

6.18   RECIPROCALS   Notice that 5/1 looks very much like the fraction 1/5. The numerator and denominator are switched. Likewise, 2/3 looks like 3/2. When we switch the numerator and denominator of a fraction, we obtain the reciprocal of the fraction.

●   The reciprocal of 7/1 is _____. The reciprocal of S^2/σ^2 is _____. The reciprocal of 1/1 is _____. What positive number equals its reciprocal? _____

1/7

σ^2/S^2 1/1

1

6.19   RECIPROCALS   Let's look at the following scale:

Notice that 4 is to the right of 3; hence $4 > 3$. Also, $3 > 2$ and $2 > 1$. We can summarize this in one expression, $4 > 3 > 2 > 1$. Also notice that $1/4 < 1/3$, $1/3 < 1/2$, and $1/2 < 1$. This can be listed as follows:

$$4 > 3 \quad \text{and} \quad 1/4 < 1/3$$
$$3 > 2 \quad \text{and} \quad 1/3 < 1/2$$
$$2 > 1 \quad \text{and} \quad 1/2 < 1 \quad \bullet$$

●   Place the correct inequality signs between the following pairs of numbers:

5   4
1/5   1/4
4   2
1/4   1/2

$5 > 4$
$1/5 < 1/4$
$4 > 2$
$1/4 < 1/2$

6.20   RULE FOR RECIPROCAL OF INEQUALITIES   The rule for taking the reciprocal of inequalities is to take the reciprocal of both sides of the inequality and change the direction of the inequality. For example, if $4 > 2$, then taking the reciprocal of both sides and changing the direction of the inequality, we have $1/4 < 1/2$. Another example, using symbols, is that if $\sigma^2/S^2 > 2$, then $S^2/\sigma^2 < 1/2$.

●   Write the reciprocals of the following inequalities:

$100 > 99$ _____
$S/\sigma > 1$ _____
$2/3 > 1/2$ _____

$1/100 < 1/99$
$\sigma/S < 1/1$
$3/2 < 2/1$

6.21   RULE FOR RECIPROCAL OF INEQUALITIES   When taking the reciprocals of inequalities, it is important to express both sides as fractions. For example, to take the reciprocal of the inequality $3 + 1/2 < 4$ we must express both $3 + 1/2$ and 4 as fractions. Thus $3 + 1/2$ would be written as $7/2$ and 4 as $4/1$. The inequality then becomes $7/2 < 4/1$, and its reciprocal becomes $2/7 > 1/4$.

- Derive a second inequality from $1 + 1/4 < 2$ by taking reciprocals of both sides (remember to first express *both* sides *exclusively* as fractions). ⎯⎯⎯⎯⎯

$4/5 > 1/2$

Review: Chapter 6

6.1   Compute:

$$(1)(-1) = \underline{\hspace{1cm}}$$
$$(-1)(-1) = \underline{\hspace{1cm}}$$
$$(-1)(-1)(-1) = \underline{\hspace{1cm}}$$
$$(-1)^2 = \underline{\hspace{1cm}}$$
$$(-5)^2 = \underline{\hspace{1cm}}$$

-1
1
-1
1
25

6.2   If $X = 3$ and $\overline{X} = 4$, then $(X - \overline{X})^2 = \underline{\hspace{1cm}}$.

1

6.3   Complete the following inequalities:
(a) $5 < 6$ and $1/5 \underline{\hspace{1cm}} 1/6$
(b) $10 < 20$ and $-10 \underline{\hspace{1cm}} -20$
(c) $7 > 1$ and $-7 \underline{\hspace{1cm}} -1$

(a) $>$
(b) $>$
(c) $<$

6.4   The reciprocal of 7 is ⎯⎯⎯.

$1/7$

6.5   If $S^2/\sigma^2 < 5$, then $\sigma^2/S^2 \underline{\hspace{1cm}} 1/5$.

$>$

6.6   If $X - \mu < 10$, then $\mu - X \underline{\hspace{1cm}} -10$.

$>$

6.7   Consider the inequality $(X - \mu)/\sigma < 2$. σ is always positive; therefore $(X - \mu)(< or >)2\sigma$ and $X(< or >)$ $\mu + 2\sigma$.

$<, <$

6.8   Derive a second inequality from $2 + 7/8 < 3$ (by taking reciprocals of both sides). ⎯⎯⎯⎯⎯

$8/23 > 1/3$

6.9   On the following scale circle a number which is greater than 3.

$$\begin{array}{ccccccccc}
-4 & -3 & -2 & -1 & 0 & 1 & 2 & 3 & 4
\end{array}$$

4

6.10   Obtain an additional inequality from the inequality $X > 3$ by multiplying both sides of the inequality by (-1).
_____

$-X < -3$

Preview Questions: Chapter 7

7.1   How many whole numbers satisfy the inequality $8 \geq X \geq 5$ which also satisfy the inequality $8 > X > 5$? ____

2

7.2   Find an alternative way of expressing the inequality $X < 8$. _____

$X \not\geq 8$

7.3   If the symbol X represents a whole number which appears along the axis given within the shaded area below, then give an inequality which describes X. _____

$X > 3$

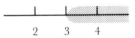

2   3   4

7.4   Is the length of the interval $5 < X < 7$ the same as the length of the interval $5 \leq X \leq 7$? _____

yes

7.5   Describe the interval 6 ± 8 by means of inequalities. _____

$-2 \leq X \leq 14$
or
$-2 < X < 14$

7.6   How long is the interval 892 ± 60? ____

120

Chapter 7

Inequality Vocabulary

We investigated properties of single inequalities in Chapter 6. In the first section of this chapter, some new inequality signs are defined, and in the second section, they are used as a way to describe intervals. The concepts of this chapter will be helpful in understanding the statistical topics of determining sample size and of estimating confidence intervals for the mean.

A: NEW INEQUALITY SYMBOLS

7.1   INEQUALITY DEFINITION   In Chapter 3 an equation was defined as "a symbolic way of writing a sentence in which the main verb is 'equals.' "   We can change this to a definition of an inequality by simply changing the verb "equals" to (1) less than, (2) greater than, (3) less than or equal to, or (4) greater than or equal to.

● Which two phrases in the above list contain the verb that is used to express equality? _____
_____

less than or equal to,
greater than or equal to

7.2   TWO TYPES OF INEQUALITIES   The distinction between the phrase "less than" and the phrase "less than or equal to" is obvious.   If an unknown, symbolized by X, were *less than* 2, this unknown could be $3/2$, 1, or $-1,000$ or it could even be a number very close to 2, say 1.99999, but it could not be exactly 2.   On the other hand, if we know that X is *less than or equal to* 2, we know that possible values for X include 2.

● Which number is less than or equal to 10.5 but is not less than 10.5? _____

10.5

7.3   "LESS THAN OR EQUAL TO" SIGN   The sign for "less than or equal to" is a combination of the sign for equality and the sign which represents the term "less than."   The "less than" sign is $<$, the equal sign is $=$, and the "less than or equal to" sign is $\leq$.

● Name all the positive whole numbers which satisfy the inequality $X \leq 5$. _____ Name all the positive whole numbers which satisfy the inequality $X < 5$.
_____

1, 2, 3, 4, 5

1, 2, 3, 4

7.4   "GREATER THAN OR EQUAL TO" SIGN   Just as the "greater than" sign $(>)$ is simply a reversed "less than" sign $(<)$, the sign for "greater than or equal to" is a reversed "less than or equal to" sign.

● The sign for "less than or equal to" is $\leq$.   What do you think the sign for "greater than or equal to" is? _____

$\geqq$

7.5   INEQUALITY SIGNS   The sign $\geqq$ is sometimes encountered in textbooks as simply $\geq$.   The two signs have the same meaning.

● Write an alternative sign for $\leqq$. _____

$\leq$

7.6   UNKNOWNS   Inequalities and equations are representations of sentences in which the main verb is either $=$, $<$, $>$, $\leqq$, or $\geqq$.   There are also usually several symbols and numbers in an equation or inequality, but one symbol is considered apart from the others. This is the symbol which is "solved for" in equations. By convention this symbol is called "the unknown" even though there may be other symbols in the equation whose values are not known. Typically, but not always, the unknown is represented by X or Y.

● Specify "the unknowns" in the following equation and inequality:

$$X + 2 = 3 \qquad \underline{\hspace{2cm}}$$
$$3 \leq X - 5 \qquad \underline{\hspace{2cm}}$$

X
X

7.7 UNKNOWNS An equation or an inequality specifies the values which the unknown can satisfy. The solution of an inequality provides limits to the permissible values of the unknown.

● In the inequality $3 \leq X - 5$, what is the smallest value that X can take on? $\underline{\hspace{1cm}}$

8

7.8 RANGE OF VALUES Suppose one is considering observations of the length of stride of adult males. An arbitrary length will be specified by X. From a practical standpoint, all numbers are *not* possible values of X. In fact, by definition, $X > 0$. The experimenter could specify $X \geq 1$ foot and $X \leq 4$ feet. Why would this specification be useful? One answer to this question is that the experimenter may wish to analyze his data on a computer, and although they are very fast, computers usually are not programmed to check the answers for reasonableness. An answer of 1,000 feet for the length of stride would be considered unreasonable by an experimenter, but not by a computer unless bounds on the plausible range of values were spelled out.

● Give reasonable inequalities satisfied by the weight of a newborn infant in pounds. $\underline{\hspace{2cm}}$

$0 < X \leq 15$ or other positive values

7.9 NEGATION OF INEQUALITY AND EQUALITY SIGNS There are also signs for "not less than," "not equal to," "not greater than or equal to," and so on. These signs are formed quite simply by using a slash. The sign for "not less than" is $\not<$, that for "not equal to" is $\neq$, that for "not greater than or equal to" is $\not\geq$, and so on.

● What sign do you think is used to represent the phrase "not greater than"? $\underline{\hspace{1cm}}$

$\not>$

7.10 RELATIONSHIPS OF INEQUALITIES AND EQUATIONS There are many useful relationships between inequalities and equations. For example, the pair of inequalities $X \geq 3$ and $X \leq 3$, considered together, are equivalent to the equation $X = 3$.

In other words, the only X which is both greater than or equal to 3 and less than or equal to 3 is 3 itself.

- Give a combination of inequalities that can be used to represent the equation $X = 10$. _____ Give a combination of inequalities that can be used to represent the expression $X \neq 10$. _____

$$X \leq 10 \qquad X \geq 10$$

$$X > 10 \qquad X < 10$$

7.11 RELATIONSHIP BETWEEN INEQUALITY SIGNS Several pairs of seemingly different inequality signs really represent the same thing. For example, if $X \not< 3$ (X is not less than 3) then X can only be greater or else equal to 3. Thus $\not<$ really says the same thing as $\geq$.

- Write two ways of saying in signs that X is less than 2. _____ _____

$$X < 2 \qquad X \not\geq 2$$

B: TWO WAYS TO DESCRIBE INTERVALS

7.12 INEQUALITIES AS RANGE FOR AN UNKNOWN If we have the inequality $3 \leq X$, then we can describe the possible values of X by the use of a number scale similar to those used earlier.

$$X \quad \underset{0 \quad 1 \quad 2 \quad 3 \quad 4}{\rule{3cm}{0pt}}$$

The unknown, X, can take on any values in the shaded area.

- Shade values on the number scale which X can take on for the inequality $X \leq 5$.

$$\underset{3 \quad 4 \quad 5}{\rule{2cm}{0pt}}$$

5

7.13 INEQUALITIES AS RANGE FOR AN UNKNOWN We can describe the unknown by using two inequality signs together in the same expression. For example, $3 \leq X \leq 5$ says that the range of values of X is from 3 to 5, and includes the values 3 and 5.

- Shade in the permissible values for X on the following number scale which satisfy the inequality $3 \leq X \leq 5$.

$$2 \quad 3 \quad 4 \quad 5 \quad 6$$

3   4   5

What are the whole numbers which satisfy the inequality $3 \leq X \leq 5$? _____

3, 4, 5

7.14   ANOTHER RANGE FOR UNKNOWNS   Another way of expressing the range for an unknown is to use inequalities of the form $3 < X < 5$. Notice that the unknown cannot assume the values 3 and 5. The number scale below pictures the possible range of X values.

- What are the whole numbers which satisfy the above inequality? _____ Is 3.000001 a permissible value of X? _____

4
yes

7.15   INTERVALS   The shaded area of the number scale below is called an interval. It represents all numbers which satisfy the inequality $3 \leqq X \leqq 5$.

- Shade in the interval which represents the inequality $3 < X < 5$.

3 4 5

Suppose X is in the shaded area as follows:

1 2 3 4

Write an expression, using inequality symbols, which expresses this interval. _____

$1 < X < 4$

7.15   END POINTS   In the expression $3 \leqq X \leqq 5$, the numbers 3 and 5 are called end points. In this case the end points are *included* in the interval. The two numbers, 3 and 5, are also called end points in the expression $3 < X < 5$, but they are *not* included in the interval.

- If $A < X < B$, are A and B both included in the interval? _____ What are the end points of the interval? _____

no
A and B

7.17   MIDPOINT   We can describe an interval with end points, 1 and 5, as $1 \leqq X \leqq 5$. This can be pictured as

We define the midpoint of this interval as the value halfway between the two end points.

- What is the midpoint of the interval $1 \leqq X \leqq 5$? ____

3

7.18 MIDPOINT When the end points are not included in an interval—for example, $3 < X < 5$—the midpoint of this interval is still defined as the value halfway between the two end points.

- What is the midpoint of the interval $3 < X < 5$? _____
  What is the midpoint of the interval $3 \leq X \leq 5$? _____

4
4

7.19 END POINTS IN TERMS OF MIDPOINTS It is convenient to express an interval in terms of its midpoint and the distance from its midpoint to its end points. For example, the interval $1 \leq X \leq 7$ has a midpoint at 4, and the distance from the midpoint to either end point is 3 ($7 - 4 = 3$ or $4 - 1 = 3$). We can describe the upper end point as $4 + 3$ and the lower end point as $4 - 3$.

- For the interval $3 \leq X \leq 7$, what is the midpoint? _____ What is the distance from the midpoint to either end point? _____ Express the upper end point in terms of the midpoint and the distance to the end point. _____

5
2

$5 + 2$

7.20 INTERVAL IN TERMS OF MIDPOINT AND DISTANCE TO END POINT An interval such as $3 \leq X \leq 9$ can be expressed in terms of its midpoint and the distance from the midpoint to the end points, i.e., midpoint minus distance and midpoint plus distance. Thus the interval $3 \leq X \leq 9$ is the same as the interval $6 - 3$ to $6 + 3$.

- What is another way to express the interval $0 \leq X \leq 10$? _____

$5 - 5$ to $5 + 5$

7.21 INTERVALS USING $\pm$ SIGN Instead of expressing an interval as $10 - 5$ and $10 + 5$, we can write 10 ± 5 and avoid writing the numbers twice. The sign $\pm$ is read "plus or minus." Thus the expression 10 ± 5, represents an interval with a midpoint at 10 and a distance from midpoint to end points of 5.

- What are the end points of the interval 6 ± 3? _____
  Express the interval $6 \leq X \leq 10$, using the $\pm$ sign. _____

3, 9

8 ± 2

7.22 LENGTH OF INTERVAL It is important to distinguish between the distance from midpoint to end point on the one hand, and the length of the interval on the other.

- The distance from the midpoint to an end point of the interval 765 ± 30 is _____. The length of the interval 765 ± 30 is _____. The distance from the midpoint to an end point is 30 and the length of the interval is 60. Notice that the length of the interval is _____ times the distance.

30
60

two

7.23 RELATIONSHIP BETWEEN DISTANCE AND LENGTH OF IN-
TERVAL   If D is the distance from midpoint to end point, and
L is the length of the interval, then $L = 2D$.

- The interval $1 \leq X \leq 9$ is given. The length of the
interval is ____.   The midpoint is ____.   The distance from the midpoint to the end point is ____.
$8 = (2)$ times ____.   Given the interval $1 \leq X \leq 6$,
the midpoint is ____, the length is ____, and the distance is ____.

8	5
4	
4	
3.5	5
2.5	

Review: Chapter 7

7.1   How many positive whole numbers satisfy the inequality
$1 \leq X \leq 10$? ____

10

7.2   How many positive whole numbers satisfy the inequality
$1 < X < 10$? ____

8

7.3   Give reasonable inequalities satisfied by measurements
of ages of elementary school students. ____

possibly $5 \leq X \leq 12$

7.4   Is there a number which satisfies the inequality $X \leq 15$
and also $X \geq 15$? ____

yes

7.5   Is there a number which satisfies the inequality $X < 15$
and also $X > 15$? ____

no

7.6   If $1 \leq X \leq 5$ and $X \neq 4$, what are the possible whole-
number values of X? ____

$1, 2, 3, 5$

7.7   Using the $\geq$ sign, express the relationship $X \not< 2$ in
another fashion. ____

$X \geq 2$

7.8   Write two expressions for the interval which starts at
one and ends with five. ____ and ____

$1 \leq X \leq 5$ 3 ± 2

7.9   Write the relationship between length of an interval
(L) and distance from midpoint to end point (D). ____

$L = 2D$

8.1   If $X = 0.04$, then

(a) $\sqrt{X} >$ ____   (e) 0.2 ____ 0.04

(b) $\sqrt{X}$ ____ 1 (f) X^2 ____ X

(c) $\sqrt{X}$ ____ 0 (g) $X^2 =$ _____

(d) $\sqrt{X} =$ ____   (h) 0.0016 ____ 0.04

8.2   Evaluate the expression $\sqrt{2 + 2}$. ____

8.3   Evaluate the expression $\sqrt{X^2 + 7}$ if $X = 3$. ____

8.4   If $X = a + b$, does $X^2 = a^2 + b^2$? _____ [yes or no]

8.5   If $0 < X < 1$, then X ____ X^2 and X ____ $\sqrt{X}$.

8.6   If X is greater than one, then X ____ X^2 and X ____ $\sqrt{X}$.

Answers (margin):

X	$>$
$<$	$<$
$>$	0.0016
0.2	$<$
	2
	4
	no
$>$	$<$
$<$	
$>$	

Chapter

8

Squares and Square Roots

In this chapter, we consider the operations of squaring and taking square roots. The first section presents a discussion of the size of the squares of numbers between zero and one, and of numbers greater than one. The second section deals with square roots of these two groups of numbers. In the third section, rules for the magnitude of squares and square roots are given. This chapter will prove helpful in the statistical topics of variance and standard deviation.

A: SQUARING

8.1 MULTIPLICATION IS REPEATED ADDITION Multiplication expresses repeated addition. For example, when we write $10 + 10 = 2(10)$ we use the number 2 to express the number of 10s that are added together.

- If we have the observations $X_1 = 4$, $X_2 = 4$, and $X_3 = 4$, and we want $\sum_{i=1}^{3} X_i$, we can use multiplication. The frequency of the observations is _____.
  The value of each observation is _____.
  The sum can be obtained by multiplying (_____)
  (_____) = _____. Alternatively, we could add the value 4 _____ times.

3
4
(3)
(4) 12
three

8.2 EXPONENTIATION AS REPEATED MULTIPLICATION The operation which expresses repeated multiplication is called exponentiation. We saw before that $10 + 10 = (2)(10)$. To symbolize repeated multiplication such as $(10)(10)$ we use the exponent 2 and write it as $(10)^2$. We can read this as 10 *raised* to the *second power*. An exponent is the value to which a number or a symbol is raised.

- The expression $(X)(X)(X)$ can also be written as _____. The exponent is _____.

X^3 3

8.3 USE OF THE EXPONENT 2 When we use the exponent 2, we are squaring a number or symbol. For example, the symbol X used with an exponent 2 is X^2 or X squared. The exponent 2, or squaring, is frequently used in elementary statistics.

- In the formula for the variance,

$$S^2 = \frac{\sum_{i=1}^{n} (X_i - \overline{X})^2}{n - 1}$$

what is the exponent? _____

2

8.4 SIZE OF SQUARES There are only two numbers which equal their own squares. One of them is zero:

$$(0)(0) = (0)^2 = 0$$

- What other number equals its own square? _____

1

8.5 SIZE OF SQUARES Zero and one are the only numbers that equal their own squares. The squares of all other numbers must be either larger or smaller than the numbers themselves. An understanding of the effect of squaring can help prevent mistakes in computation which frequently appear in any long series of calculations. The errors can, in the case of squaring, often be detected when the size of the square appears to be of the wrong magnitude. For example, mistakes in squaring frequently occur when decimals such as 0.1 are squared. Notice that $(0.1)^2 = (0.1)(0.1)$ which is the same as $(1/10)(1/10)$. In words, the expression $(1/10)(1/10)$ can be expressed as one-tenth of one-tenth. When only one-tenth of a quantity is considered, this part must be smaller than the quantity itself. Therefore $(0.1)^2$ must be smaller than 0.1.

● $(0.2)^2$ must be smaller than _____. What is the value of $(0.2)^2$? _____

0.2
0.04

8.6 SQUARES OF NUMBERS BETWEEN ZERO AND ONE The square of X, when X is any number $0 < X < 1$, satisfies the inequality $X^2 < X$. This is true for the following reasons:

1. Since X is a positive number, we can multiply by X both sides of the inequality $X < 1$ without changing the direction of the inequality sign.

2. If we perform this multiplication, we have $(X)(X) < (X)(1)$, or $X^2 < X$. Therefore we know that the square of a number less than one is smaller than the number itself.

● Square the following numbers, then express the relationship between the number and its square as in the first example.

X	X^2	Relation between X^2 and X
0.2	0.04	$0.04 < 0.2$
0.01	_____	_____
0.1	_____	_____
1.0	_____	_____
10.0	_____	_____
100.0	_____	_____

$0.0001 < 0.01$
$0.01 < 0.1$
$1.0 = 1.0$
$100 > 10$
$10,000 > 100$

8.7 SQUARES OF NUMBERS GREATER THAN ONE The square of X when X is any number greater than 1 is always greater than X itself; that is, if $X > 1$, then $X^2 > X$.

● What is the square of 1.01? _____ In this problem is $X^2 > X$? _____ If $X = 1.0000001$, is $X^2 > X$? _____

1.0201
yes
yes

B: THE SQUARE ROOT

8.8 PAIRS OF OPERATIONS In solving an equation, the operations are considered in pairs. Thus subtraction is paired with addition, and division is paired with multiplication.

- To solve the equation $X + 2 = 9$, we _____ 2 from both sides of the equation. To solve the equation $2X = 9$, we _____ both sides of the equation by 2.

8.9 SQUARE ROOT SIGN Given the equation $X^2 = 9$, we know that a number X, when squared, equals 9. To solve this equation for X, we apply the opposite operation from squaring, that of taking the square root, which is symbolized by the sign $\sqrt{}$. For example, $X^2 = 9$ is solved by taking the square root of both sides, $\sqrt{X^2} = \sqrt{9}$ or $X = 3$. (It should be noted that $X = -3$ is another possible solution to this equation.)

- $\sqrt{X^2} = $ _____
  $\sqrt{9} = $ _____
  $(\sqrt{X})^2 = $ _____

8.10 OPERATIONS WITHIN THE SQUARE ROOT SIGN Just as with parentheses, all operations within the square root sign must be performed before the square root of the result is taken. For example, $\sqrt{9 + 16} = \sqrt{25} = 5$.

- $\sqrt{9} = $ _____
  $\sqrt{16} = $ _____
  Does $\sqrt{9} + \sqrt{16} = \sqrt{9 + 16}$? _____

8.11 SOLVING EQUATIONS WHICH CONTAIN SQUARE ROOTS Consider the equation frequently found in elementary statistics,

$$Z = \frac{\overline{X} - \mu}{\sigma / \sqrt{n}}$$

Suppose we want to solve for n. First we multiply both sides of the equation by $\sigma/\sqrt{n}$, obtaining

$$\frac{Z\sigma}{\sqrt{n}} = \overline{X} - \mu$$

Next we multiply both sides of the equation by $\sqrt{n}$, obtaining

$$Z\sigma = \sqrt{n}\,(\overline{X} - \mu)$$

and dividing both sides by $(\overline{X} - \mu)$, we obtain

$$\sqrt{n} = \frac{Z\sigma}{\overline{X} - \mu}$$

To obtain a solution for n we must square both sides of the equation:

$$(\sqrt{n})^2 = \left(\frac{Z\sigma}{\overline{X} - \mu}\right)^2$$

Notice that we must square the entire right-hand side.

- $(\sqrt{n})^2 = $ _____

C: MAGNITUDE OF SQUARE ROOTS

8.12 REVIEW OF SIZE OF SQUARES   In actual computations involving square roots, it is useful to have some general idea of the magnitude of the square root of a number in relation to the size of the number itself.   In Section A we showed that if $X < 1$, then $X^2 < X$, and if $X > 1$, then $X^2 > X$.

- $0.5 < 1$; therefore $(0.5)^2$ _____ 0.5.
  $5 > 1$; therefore $(5)^2$ _____ 5.

8.13 SQUARE ROOTS AS OPPOSITE OF SQUARES   Because the square root is the operation opposite to the squaring operation, it seems reasonable to suspect that it will have some properties opposite to the properties of the square.   In the first section of this chapter the positive numbers were separated into two groups.   The first contained numbers less than one.   The squares of these numbers were less than the numbers themselves.   The second group contained numbers greater than one, whose squares were greater than the numbers themselves.   We will see that the properties of these groups of numbers are reversed when we consider the square root operation.

- On the number scale here, circle the part of the scale which represents those numbers which satisfy the inequality $X^2 < X$.

  ⌐ ⌐ ⌐ ⌐ ─────

  0   1   2   3

  What is the smallest number which does *not* satisfy the inequality $X^2 < X$? _____

8.14 SIZE OF SQUARE ROOTS   Let's actually write the inequality of the previous frame above the appropriate part of the number scale.

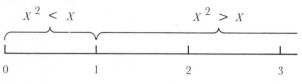

$$X^2 < X \qquad\qquad X^2 > X$$

0   1   2   3

Now suppose it is permissible to take the square root of both sides of an inequality without changing the inequality sign. Since $\sqrt{X^2} = X$, we obtain

$$X < \sqrt{X} \qquad\qquad X > \sqrt{X}$$

0   1   2   3

Between (but not including) 0 and 1, $X < \sqrt{X}$ and $X^2 < X$.

- If $X = 23$, then 23 _____ $\sqrt{23}$ and 23 _____ 23^2.

8.15 SQUARE ROOT OF BOTH SIDES OF AN INEQUALITY How can we justify taking the square root of both sides of positive inequalities and not changing the inequality sign? Let's examine the reason for calling X^2, "X squared." The number X can be considered a length, and X^2 (or X times X) can be considered the area of a square whose sides have length X. Let us write the inequality $X^2 < Y^2$, where X and Y are any positive numbers which satisfy this inequality. We can also think of Y^2 as the area of a square whose side is of length Y. Now, $X^2 < Y^2$ signifies that the area of the square whose sides are X is smaller than the area of the square whose sides are Y.

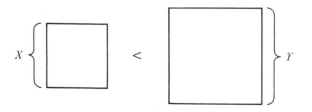

Therefore, if $X^2 < Y^2$, then $X < Y$, and we can take the square root of both sides of the inequality without changing the inequality sign.

- If $0 < X < 1$, then $X^2 < X$. Because X is the same as $(\sqrt{X})(\sqrt{X})$, we can write $X^2 < (\sqrt{X})(\sqrt{X})$. We know that if $X^2 < Y^2$, then $X < Y$ for any positive X and Y. What should we set equal to Y in the relationship $X^2 < (\sqrt{X})(\sqrt{X})$? _____ If X is a positive number between 0 and 1, then X _____ $\sqrt{X}$.

$\sqrt{X}$
<

8.16 SQUARE ROOTS OF NUMBERS BETWEEN ZERO AND ONE If $0 < X < 1$, then the square root of X is greater than X. For example, $\sqrt{1/4} = 1/2$.

- Is $1/2 > 1/4$? _____ Is $\sqrt{1/4}$ less than $1/4$? _____ The expression $\sqrt{1/9} =$ _____. Is $1/3$ greater than $1/9$? _____

yes
no 1/3
yes

8.17 EXAMPLE OF SIZE OF SQUARE ROOTS Now let's look at the size of the square roots of various numbers. The square root of 4 is 2. The square root of the reciprocal of 4, 1/4, is 1/2. Notice that $4 > 2$, while $1/4 < 1/2$.

- It is given that $\sqrt{9} = 3$ and $\sqrt{1/9} = 1/3$. The square root of 1/9 is greater than 1/9, but the square root of 9 is _____ than 9.

less

8.18 SQUARE ROOTS OF NUMBERS GREATER THAN ONE If $X > 1$, then the square root of X is less than X. We know that $X^2 > X$ if $X > 1$. Taking the square root of both sides of the inequality results in $X > \sqrt{X}$ or, reversing the inequality, $\sqrt{X} < X$.

- If $X = 4$,
$$\sqrt{X} = \underline{\hspace{1cm}} \quad \text{and} \quad 2 \underline{\hspace{1cm}} 4$$
If $X = 1$,
$$\sqrt{X} = \underline{\hspace{1cm}}$$

2 $<$

1

8.19 SQUARE ROOTS OF NUMBERS GREATER THAN ONE The square root of any number greater than one is less than the number but is still greater than one. In symbols, if $X > 1$, then $1 < \sqrt{X} < X$.

- If $X = 1.001$, then $\underline{\hspace{1cm}} < \underline{\hspace{1cm}} < 1.001$.

1 $\sqrt{1.001}$

8.20 SQUARE ROOTS OF NUMBERS BETWEEN ZERO AND ONE The square root of any number between zero and one is greater than the number itself, but still lies between zero and one. In symbols, if $0 < X < 1$, then $1 > \sqrt{X} > 0$ and $\sqrt{X} > X$.

- $\sqrt{0} = \underline{\hspace{1cm}}$, $\sqrt{1} = \underline{\hspace{1cm}}$, $\sqrt{1/4} = \underline{\hspace{1cm}}$. Does $\sqrt{1/4}$ lie between 0 and 1? $\underline{\hspace{1cm}}$ Is $\sqrt{1/4}$ greater or less than 1/4? $\underline{\hspace{1cm}}$

0 1 1/2
yes
greater

8.21 REVIEW OF MAGNITUDE OF SQUARES AND SQUARE ROOTS If $0 < X < 1$, then $X^2 < X$ and $\sqrt{X} > X$, and both X^2 and $\sqrt{X}$ lie between 0 and 1. If $X > 1$, then $X^2 > X$ and $\sqrt{X} < X$, and both X^2 and $\sqrt{X}$ are greater than 1. If $X = 0$ or $X = 1$, then $X^2 = \sqrt{X} = X$.

Review: Chapter 8

8.1 In taking the square root of $4 + 5$ or in computing $\sqrt{4 + 5}$, the first operation to be performed is $\underline{\hspace{1cm}}$. $\sqrt{4 + 5} = \sqrt{\underline{\hspace{1cm}}} = \underline{\hspace{1cm}}$.

addition
9 3

8.2 If $X = a^2 + b^2$, then $\sqrt{X} = \underline{\hspace{1cm}}$.

$\sqrt{a^2 + b^2}$

8.3 If $\sqrt{X + 1} = 3$, what is X? $\underline{\hspace{1cm}}$

8

8.4 If $X = 0.09$, then
$$\sqrt{X} > \underline{\hspace{1cm}} \qquad 0.3 \underline{\hspace{1cm}} 0.09$$
$$\sqrt{X} \underline{\hspace{1cm}} 1 \qquad X^2 \underline{\hspace{1cm}} X$$
$$\sqrt{X} \underline{\hspace{1cm}} 0 \qquad X^2 = \underline{\hspace{1cm}}$$
$$\sqrt{X} = \underline{\hspace{1cm}} \qquad 0.0081 \underline{\hspace{1cm}} 0.09$$

X $>$
$<$ $<$
$>$ 0.0081
0.3 $<$

8.5 If $X = 1/4$, then $\sqrt{X} = \underline{\hspace{1cm}}$, $X^2 = \underline{\hspace{1cm}}$. Then $X^2 \underline{\hspace{1cm}} X \underline{\hspace{1cm}} \sqrt{X}$.

1/2 1/16
$<$ $<$

8.6 If $X = 4$, then $\sqrt{X} = \underline{\hspace{1cm}}$, $X^2 = \underline{\hspace{1cm}}$.

2 16

Preview Questions: Chapter 9

Find the square roots of the following numbers, using the square root table appearing in the back of this book.

9.1   0.000925 _____   0.030414

9.2   0.00925   _____   0.096177

9.3   0.06210   _____   0.24920

9.4   17.4   _____   4.1713

9.5   8,764   _____   93.595

9.6   For $n_1 = 4$ and $n_2 = 10$, compute

$$\sqrt{\frac{1}{n_1} + \frac{1}{n_2}} = \text{_____}$$ 0.59161

9.7   With $S^2 = 817.4$, find a value for S. _____   28.583

Chapter 9

Use of Square Root Table

This chapter deals primarily with use of tables of square roots. Before you start this chapter, review Chapter 8, which contains a general description of square roots and their magnitude.

This program has been written using the square root table given at the end of this book. We recommend that you use this table to learn the material in this program; when you become more familiar with the use of square root tables, you should be able to transfer what you have learned to any other square root table.

Becoming familiar with the process of taking square roots will aid you in calculating the standard deviation, which is a common computation in elementary statistics.

A: INTRODUCTION TO THE USE OF THE SQUARE ROOT TABLE

For this section, turn to the square root table beginning on page 143.

9.1 PARTS OF THE TABLE This table can be divided into three separate parts:

1. The first vertical column on the left, containing numbers such as 1.0 and 10.
2. The first horizontal row across the top of the page, containing numbers such as 0, 1, 2, . . . , 9
3. Finally, the body of the table

- What is the first number in the first column on the left-hand side of page 143? _____ What is the first number in the body of the table? _____ What is the square root of 1? _____

1.0
1.0000
1

9.2 CONTINUATION OF PAGES Looking only at page 143, we see that the numbers in the first column on the left side of the page run from 1.0 or 10. to 2.4 or 24. The next page is a continuation of this table, in which the numbers in the first column run from 2.5 or 25. to 3.9 or 39. The table continues to page 148.

- If you look for the number 48 in the first column, which page will it be found on? _____

page 145

9.3 USE OF THE TOP ROW There are only one-digit and two-digit numbers in the first column. If we use the table to take square roots of numbers with three digits or more, we have to take into account the numbers in the first horizontal row (0, 1, 2, . . . , 9) across the top of the page.

- Do you take the first row into account if you want the square root of 934? _____ [yes or no] Do you take the first row into account if you want the square root of 17? _____ [yes or no]

yes

no

9.4 USE OF THE TOP ROW To take the square root of 16.3, we would locate the 16 in the first vertical column to the left and the 3 in the first row across the top of the page.

- In taking $\sqrt{24.6}$, which digit corresponds to a number in the first row of the table across the top? _____

6

9.5   SQUARE ROOT   The square root of 16.0 is 4.0.   Look for 4.0000 in the body of the table on page 143. Notice that 4.0000 is in the row beginning with 16. and in the column headed by a 0 at the top of the page.
●   The number 4.9900 at the lower right-hand side of page 143 is in the column headed _____ at the top of the page.   The row on the left-hand side begins with _____.

9

24

9.6   SQUARE ROOT   The square root of 24.9 is 4.9900.   The square root of 24.0 is 4.8990.   Thus, when we take the square root of a number which has more than two nonzero digits, we take into account its third digit by using the column headed by that digit.
●   To take the square root of 21.2, we would use the column headed at the top by _____.

2

9.7   SQUARE ROOT   You know that $\sqrt{16} = 4.0$.   To get the answer to $\sqrt{1.6}$ look in the row beginning with 1.6 and in the first column headed by 0.
● $\sqrt{1.6} =$ _____

1.2649

9.8   SQUARE ROOT   Notice that the rows seem to be paired. There is a row beginning with 1.6 and one beginning with 16, which are grouped together. $10 \times 1.6 = 16$.
●   The row immediately above the one beginning with 17 begins with _____. $10 \times 1.7 =$ _____

1.7   17

9.9   SQUARE ROOT   If we want to take the square root of a number which appears in the first column, we can find the square root directly by looking in the column headed by 0.
● $\sqrt{17} =$ _____
      $\sqrt{1.7} =$ _____

4.1231
1.3038

9.10   SQUARE ROOT   By using the different columns we can directly take the square roots of many three-digit numbers. For example, in the section of the table on page 144, $\sqrt{25.1} = 5.0100$.   This is found in the row beginning with 25 and in the column headed by 1.
● $\sqrt{36.1} =$ _____
      $\sqrt{3.61} =$ _____
      Using the part of the table on page 148, we find that $\sqrt{94.7} =$ _____.

6.0083
1.9000

9.7314

9.11   ROUNDING   The numbers whose square roots are given directly by the table go from 1 to 99.9.   We can only use the table to find the square roots of numbers of three digits or less. To find the square roots of numbers with more than three digits, we can round off to three digits and then use the table.

● Round off the following numbers so that you can find their square roots by using the table.

16.2334	_____
1.26999	_____
89.624	_____

16.2
1.27
89.6

If you have difficulty with this problem, review the round-off rules in Chapter 1.   Round off first and then find

$$\sqrt{25.61} = \underline{\hspace{2cm}}$$
$$\sqrt{1.6788} = \underline{\hspace{2cm}}$$

5.0596
1.2961

9.12   SQUARE ROOTS   The square roots of all numbers with three digits or less between 1.00 and 99.9 can be read directly from the table, using the first column and the top row.   To take the square roots of other numbers, using this table, will require further techniques.

● Which of the following numbers are we able to take square roots of directly from the table: 25.8, 1.05, 0.96, 1003, 21.68? _____

25.8, 1.05, and 21.68, if rounded

B: COUNTING DIGITS AND USING APOSTROPHES

This section will provide the background which will enable you to find square roots of numbers less than 1 or greater than 99.9.

9.13   DIGIT   A particularly important word is used in this chapter.   The word *digit* must be used consistently.   Any number from 0 to 9 will be called a digit.

● Is 8 a digit?   _____

yes

9.14   DIGITS TO LEFT OF DECIMAL POINT   In taking the square root of a number, it is important to know the number of digits to the left of the decimal point.   For example, 999.5 has three digits to the left, 1246.0 has four digits to the left, and 1,236,415.0 has seven digits to the left of the decimal point.

● How many digits are there to the left of the decimal point in

565.0565	_____	1,000.0	_____
1.1	_____	23.	_____

3   4
1   2

9.15 SQUARE ROOTS Let's look for a pattern in the square roots of the following numbers:

$$\sqrt{1} = 1$$
$$\sqrt{10} = 3.1623$$
$$\sqrt{100} = 10$$
$$\sqrt{1,000} = 31.623$$
$$\sqrt{10,000} = 100$$

● Is $\sqrt{100,000}$ equal to 1,000 or 316.23? _____

What is the $\sqrt{1,000,000}$? _____

316.23
1,000

9.16 APOSTROPHES Instead of counting the number of digits to the left of the decimal point, it is simpler to group the digits in pairs. The groups of digits are partitioned by apostrophes. Start with an apostrophe over the decimal point, and mark off in pairs. For example,

$$1346.5 = 13'46'5$$
$$100,000. = 10'00'00'$$
$$1.26 = 1'26$$
$$1,000. = 10'00'$$
$$10.00 = 10'00$$

● Try this yourself on the following numbers:

100.0	_____
160.0	_____
81.0	_____
1,600.0	_____

1'00'0
1'60'0
81'
16'00'0

9.17 DECIMAL APOSTROPHES Notice that in partitioning numbers in pairs we always start from the decimal point. The first apostrophe is called the decimal apostrophe.

● In the number 98.1, between what two digits does the decimal apostrophe go? ____ and ____

8   1

9.18 APOSTROPHES We can also partition positive numbers less than 1 into pairs of digits with apostrophes. We do this by starting with the decimal apostrophe and moving to the right. For example,

$$0.0826 = '08'26$$
$$0.000234 = '00'02'34$$
$$0.0000561 = '00'00'56'1$$

● Try this on the following numbers:

0.0915	_____
0.00026	_____
0.000521	_____

'09'15
'00'02'6
'00'05'21

9.19 DIGIT APOSTROPHES In the following numbers the apostrophe which is circled is called the *digit* apostrophe. If we can find the digit apostrophe, we will know what row of the square root table to use to find the square root of any number.

$$83Ⓞ65ꞋꞋ$$
$$1Ⓞ25ꞋꞋ$$
$$ꞋꞋ00Ꞌ36Ⓞ21$$
$$ꞋꞋ01Ⓞ36Ꞌ52$$

- In $4Ⓞ72Ꞌ56ꞋꞋ$ the digit apostrophe is between ____ and ____.

9.20 DIGIT APOSTROPHES Every digit apostrophe has a nonzero digit to its left.
- In the following numbers the digit apostrophe is circled. Indicate all the digits to the left of the digit apostrophe.

$92Ⓞ36Ꞌ54ꞋꞋ$	____
$1Ⓞ25ꞋꞋ$	____
$ꞋꞋ00Ꞌ25Ⓞ0$	_____
$ꞋꞋ01Ⓞ36Ꞌ$	____

9.21 DIGIT APOSTROPHES Perhaps you have noticed that the digit apostrophe is the apostrophe farthest to the left which still has either one or two nonzero digits to the left of it. For example,

$$10Ⓞ00Ꞌ10ꞋꞋ$$
$$2Ⓞ36ꞋꞋ$$
$$ꞋꞋ00Ꞌ00Ꞌ25Ⓞ$$
$$ꞋꞋ00Ꞌ01Ⓞ52Ꞌ$$

- Circle the digit apostrophe in the following numbers:

$$1Ꞌ23ꞋꞋ$$
$$ꞋꞋ00Ꞌ16Ꞌ50Ꞌ$$
$$12Ꞌ40ꞋꞋ$$

How many nonzero digits are always to the left of the digit apostrophe? ____ or ____ Make up an example in which the digit apostrophe is also a decimal apostrophe. _____

C: SQUARE ROOTS OF NUMBERS 100 AND GREATER

9.22 DIGIT APOSTROPHE AS A DECIMAL POINT   Suppose we put apostrophes in the number 625. We get 6Ⓞ25. In the square root table, $\sqrt{6.25} = 2.5$. Because $25^2 = 625$, we know that $\sqrt{625} = 25$ (Chapter 8). If we think of the *digit* apostrophe as a *decimal point* and use the table to find the square root, we will get the right digits, although the decimal point will be in the wrong place.

- Take the number 225. Put apostrophes in it: _____.
  From the square root table, $\sqrt{2.25} =$ _____. Now, $\sqrt{225} = 15$. Are the digits in $\sqrt{2.25}$ the same as the digits in $\sqrt{225}$? _____

2Ⓞ25.
1.5

yes

9.23 DIGIT APOSTROPHE AS A DECIMAL POINT   To take the square root of 744, we first partition it, getting 7Ⓞ44. If we think of the digit apostrophe (the one farthest to the left) as a decimal point, we can decide whether we should use row 7.4 or row 74 of the square root table. Because the digit apostrophe comes between 7 and 4, we use the row beginning with 7.4.

- Partition 625 with apostrophes. _____ The digit apostrophe is between the digits _____ and _____. To find $\sqrt{625}$, we use the row beginning with _____ in the table.

6Ⓞ25.
6   2
6.2

9.24 FIRST STEP IN SQUARE ROOTS OF LARGE NUMBERS   So far we have used the apostrophes to determine which row of the table to use. Instead of finding the square root of 625, for example, we found the square root of 6.25, thinking of the digit apostrophe as a decimal point. The first step in obtaining the square root of a large number is deciding which row of the square root table to use.

- The first step in finding the square root of a number such as 821 is to place the decimal point by locating the digit apostrophe. For 821, this would be _____.

8Ⓞ21. leading to 8.21

9.25 SECOND STEP IN SQUARE ROOTS OF LARGE NUMBERS   The second step is to find $\sqrt{821}$ from $\sqrt{8.21}$ or, in general, to find the actual square root from the square root we have looked up. To do this, we count the number of *pairs* of digits between the digit apostrophe and the decimal apostrophe. An example is 8Ⓞ23'65. Here $1 + 1 = 2$ pairs of digits between the digit apostrophe and the decimal apostrophe (the apostrophe over the decimal point).

●   Find the number of pairs of digits between the digit and the decimal apostrophe in the following numbers.

$$8^{\odot}15\text{'}26\text{.}\qquad \underline{\hspace{3em}}$$
$$15^{\odot}10\text{.}\qquad \underline{\hspace{3em}}$$
$$2^{\odot}65\text{'}41\text{'}26\text{.}\qquad \underline{\hspace{3em}}$$

2
1
3

9.26   SECOND STEP IN SQUARE ROOTS OF LARGE NUMBERS
After we have counted the number of pairs of digits, we move the decimal point in the square root one place to the right for each pair of digits.

●   How many places to the right would we move the decimal point in the square root of $8^{\odot}15\text{'}26\text{.}$?   _____

2

9.27   STEPS IN SQUARE ROOTS OF LARGE NUMBERS   To find the square root of any number greater than 100, we

    1. Place the apostrophes.

    2. Take the digit apostrophe as a decimal point and use the square root table.

    3. Count the number of pairs of digits between the digit apostrophe and the decimal apostrophe.

    4. Move the decimal point in the square root one place to the right for each pair of digits. For example, to find $\sqrt{744}$, we

    1. Place the apostrophes: $7^{\odot}44\text{.}$

    2. Look up $\sqrt{7.44} = 2.7276$.

    3. Count one pair of digits between the digit and the decimal apostrophe.

    4. Move the decimal point one place to the right, getting 27.276. Therefore $\sqrt{744} = 27.276$.

●   Find $\sqrt{822}$.

    1. Place the apostrophes in 822. _____

    2. Look up $\sqrt{8.22}$. _____

    3. How many pairs of digits are there between the decimal and digit apostrophes? _____

    4. Move the decimal point to the right.

        $\sqrt{822} =$ _____

$8^{\odot}22\text{.}$
2.8671

1

28.671

9.28 SQUARE ROOTS This process works for any number greater than 100. To find $\sqrt{185000000}$, we

1. Place the apostrophes: 1ᐤ85'00'00'00⁚
2. Find $\sqrt{1.85} = 1.3601$.
3. Count four pairs of digits between the digit apostrophe and the decimal apostrophe.
4. Move the decimal point four places to the right, resulting in $\sqrt{185000000} = 13601$.

- $\sqrt{623000} =$ _____.   789.30

9.29 SQUARE ROOTS OF NUMBERS WHICH NEED ROUNDING Suppose we are taking the square root of 6,293,478. To use the table, we first round 6,293,478 to 6,290,000, because the table only has three digits. (Because of the rounding, the resulting square root value is only an approximation. This is sometimes indicated by the use of the signs, $\approx$, $\simeq$, or $\doteq$, which mean "approximately equal to.")

- $\sqrt{6,290,000} =$ _____   2508.0
  $\sqrt{391,842} \doteq$ _____   626.10

9.30 REVIEW We have learned how to take the square root of any number greater than 1 either by using the table directly or by using the table and moving the decimal point to the right.

- What is the square root of 100? _____   10

D: SQUARE ROOTS OF NUMBERS LESS THAN ONE

9.31 APOSTROPHES To take the square root of a number less than 1, we also use apostrophes. For example, to find the square root of 0.00164, we first place the apostrophes, starting with the decimal apostrophe and moving right: 0.00164 = ⁚00'16ᐤ4. The apostrophe over the decimal point is called the decimal apostrophe. The apostrophe between 6 and 4 is the digit apostrophe. The digit apostrophe is the apostrophe farthest to the left which still has one or two nonzero digits to the left of it.

- Place apostrophes in the number 0.000182. _____   ⁚00'01ᐤ82
  The decimal apostrophe is over the _____ _____.   decimal point
  The digit apostrophe is between the digits _____ and   1
  _____.   8

9.32   DIGIT APOSTROPHE AS A DECIMAL POINT   After placing the apostrophes, we use the digit apostrophe as a decimal point to indicate what row of the table to use. For example, to find the square root of 0.000183, we

1. Place the apostrophes: '00'01⊙83.
2. Use the row of the table, starting with 1.8, and look up $\sqrt{1.83} = 1.3528$, because the digit apostrophe is between the 1 and the 8.

●   When we use the tables to take the square root of 0.00165, between which two digits do we pretend the decimal point lies? ____ and ____.

9.33   PLACING THE DECIMAL POINT IN THE ANSWER   To find $\sqrt{0.00615}$, we

    1. Place the apostrophes: '00'61⊙5.
    2. Look up $\sqrt{61.5} = 7.8422$.
    3. Place the decimal point in the answer by counting the number of pairs of digits between the decimal and digit apostrophes. In this example there are two pairs (00 and 61). We move the decimal point in 7.8422 two places to the *left*, getting $\sqrt{0.00615} = 0.078422$.

●   When we take the square root of any positive number not in the table, we count the number of pairs of digits between the _____ apostrophe and the _____ apostrophe. In which direction did we move the decimal point in the tabled square root to find the answer when the number was less than one? _____

9.34   SQUARE ROOTS OF NUMBERS LESS THAN ONE   To take the square root of 0.0009191,

1. First round off 0.0009191 to 0.000919.
2. Then place the apostrophes: '00'09⊙19.
3. Find $\sqrt{9.19} = 3.0315$.
4. Move the decimal point two places to the left, because there are two pairs of digits between the decimal and digit apostrophes.
5. Now, $\sqrt{0.000919} = 0.030315$.

●   Find $\sqrt{0.0008621}$.
    1. Round off 0.0008621 to _____.
    2. Place the apostrophes: _____.
    3. $\sqrt{} = $ _____.
    4. Count the pairs of digits: ____
    5. $\sqrt{0.000862} = $ _____.

9.35 SQUARE ROOTS Perhaps you have noticed that the steps in finding the square roots of numbers less than 1 are the same ones used in finding the square roots of numbers greater than 100, except in the final step, in which we move the decimal point. For the small numbers we moved the decimal point to the left, and for large numbers we moved the decimal point to the right.

● To take $\sqrt{0.00825}$, we move the decimal point two places to the _____ after we find $\sqrt{82.5}$.

left

E: SQUARE ROOTS IN ELEMENTARY STATISTICS

You will be taking square roots many times in doing the class exercises in statistics. This section contains examples of computations of square roots that are common to elementary statistics.

9.36 SQUARE ROOT Suppose we know what X^2 is, and we want to find out what X is. We would naturally take the square root of X^2.

● If $X^2 = 25.2$, what is X? _____

5.02

9.37 SQUARE ROOT We frequently use other letters besides X. For instance, we can use S^2. Similarly, the square root of S^2 is S.

● If $S^2 = 201.8$, what is S? _____

14.2

9.38 SQUARE ROOT OF n In this book the symbol n stands for the sample size. For instance, if we took the heights of 893 students, our sample size would be 893.

● Where the sample size is 893, compute $\sqrt{n}$. _____

29.9

9.39 SQUARE ROOT OF $1/n_1 + 1/n_2$ Sometimes in statistics we take two samples. Therefore we have two sample sizes, one for the first sample and one for the second sample. Then n_1 is the size of the first sample, and n_2 is the size of the second sample. Frequently we have to compute $\sqrt{1/n_1 + 1/n_2}$. The first step is to convert $1/n_1$ and $1/n_2$ to decimals. For example, if $n_1 = 15$ and $n_2 = 20$, then

$$1/15 = 0.0667$$
$$1/20 = 0.0500$$

We found 0.0667 by dividing 15 into 1.

● If $n_1 = 10$ and $n_2 = 40$, then $1/n_1 =$ _____ and $1/n_2 =$ _____ .

0.10
0.025

9.40 $\sqrt{1/n_1 + 1/n_2}$ After we have converted $1/n_1$ and $1/n_2$ to decimals, the second step is to get the sum of these two decimals.

● If $n_1 = 15$ and $n_2 = 20$, then $1/n_1 = 0.0667$, and $1/n_2 = 0.0500$, and the answer is

$$0.0667$$
$$+0.0500$$
$$\overline{0.1167} = 1/n_1 + 1/n_2$$

If $n_1 = 10$, and $n_2 = 40$, find $1/n_1 + 1/n_2$.

$$1/n_1 = \underline{\hspace{2cm}}$$
$$1/n_2 = \underline{\hspace{2cm}}$$

$$\underline{\hspace{3cm}}$$
$$\underline{\hspace{2cm}} = 1/n_1 + 1/n_2$$

0.10
0.025

0.125

9.41 $\sqrt{1/n_1 + 1/n_2}$ To compute $\sqrt{1/n_1 + 1/n_2}$ we (1) convert $1/n_1$ and $1/n_2$ to decimals, (2) add the two decimals, and (3) take the square root of the sum.   For example, if $n_1 = 15$, and $n_2 = 20$, then

1. $1/n_1 = 0.0667$ and $1/n_2 = 0.0500$.
2. The sum is 0.1167.
3. $\sqrt{0.1167} \doteq 0.34205 \doteq \sqrt{1/n_1 + 1/n_2} = \sqrt{1/15 + 1/20}$.

● Compute $\sqrt{1/n_1 + 1/n_2}$, where $n_1 = 4$ and $n_2 = 10$. First,

$$1/n_1 = \underline{\hspace{1.5cm}}$$
$$1/n_2 = \underline{\hspace{1.5cm}}$$

$$\underline{\hspace{3cm}}$$
$$\underline{\hspace{2cm}} = 1/n_1 + 1/n_2$$

Finally, $\sqrt{1/n_1 + 1/n_2} = \underline{\hspace{2cm}}$.

0.25
0.10

0.350

0.59161

Review: Chapter 9

Use a table of square roots to answer the following problems.

9.1   Find the square roots of the following numbers:

$$\sqrt{7.82} = \underline{\hspace{2cm}}$$
$$\sqrt{15.0} = \underline{\hspace{2cm}}$$
$$\sqrt{75} = \underline{\hspace{2cm}}$$
$$\sqrt{83.2} = \underline{\hspace{2cm}}$$

2.7964
3.8730
8.6603
9.1214

9.2   After rounding, find the square roots of the following numbers:

$$\sqrt{3.977} \doteq \underline{\hspace{2cm}}$$ 1.9950
$$\sqrt{6.655} \doteq \underline{\hspace{2cm}}$$ 2.5807
$$\sqrt{79.54} \doteq \underline{\hspace{2cm}}$$ 8.9163
$$\sqrt{64.75} \doteq \underline{\hspace{2cm}}$$ 8.0498

9.3   Find the square root of the following large numbers:

$$\sqrt{109} = \underline{\hspace{2cm}}$$ 10.440
$$\sqrt{563} = \underline{\hspace{2cm}}$$ 23.728
$$\sqrt{10,682} \doteq \underline{\hspace{2cm}}$$ 103.44
$$\sqrt{362,789} \doteq \underline{\hspace{2cm}}$$ 602.49
$$\sqrt{789.25} \doteq \underline{\hspace{2cm}}$$ 28.089

9.4   Find the square root of the following small numbers:

$$\sqrt{0.64} = \underline{\hspace{1cm}}$$ 0.8
$$\sqrt{0.561} = \underline{\hspace{2cm}}$$ 0.749
$$\sqrt{0.0163} = \underline{\hspace{2cm}}$$ 0.12767
$$\sqrt{0.03456} \doteq \underline{\hspace{2cm}}$$ 0.18601
$$\sqrt{0.0000845} = \underline{\hspace{2cm}}$$ 0.0091924
$$\sqrt{0.0003} = \underline{\hspace{2cm}}$$ 0.017321

9.5   With $n_1 = 10$ and $n_2 = 5$, find $\sqrt{1/n_1 + 1/n_2}$.

$$\sqrt{1/n_1 + 1/n_2} = \underline{\hspace{2cm}}$$ 0.54772

Preview Questions: Chapter 10

10.1 Which of the following expressions are valid and which are invalid?

$2(X + Y) = 2X + 2Y$ _____   valid

$(X + Y)^2 = X^2 + Y^2$ _____   invalid

$2 + X + Y = X + 2 + Y + 2$ _____   invalid

$X(X + Y) + Y(X + Y) = (X + Y)^2$ _____   valid

10.2 Which of the following expressions is valid?

(a) $(X_i - \overline{X})^2 + 2\overline{X}(X_i - \overline{X}) + \overline{X}^2 = X_i^2$

(b) $(X_i - \overline{X})^2 + 2\overline{X}(X_i - \overline{X}) + \overline{X}^2 = 0$

      _____   (a)

10.3 Is $\sum_{i=1}^{n} (X_i^2 - 2\overline{X}X_i + \overline{X}^2) = \sum_{i=1}^{n} (X_i - \overline{X})^2$?   _____   yes

10.4 Is $\sum_{i=1}^{n} \overline{X}X_i = n\overline{X}^2$?   _____   yes

10.5 Is $\sum_{i=1}^{n} (X_i - \overline{X})^2 = \sum_{i=1}^{n} X_i^2 - n\overline{X}^2$?   _____   yes

Chapter

10

Alternative Formulas for the Variance

This chapter relates directly to statistics and describes various ways of computing the variance. In Section A, we describe the different forms that the square of a sum can take. This is done algebraically and pictorially. The results of Section A are used to develop alternative formulas for the variance S^2. In Section B, three formulas for the variance are derived and their properties explained.

A: SQUARING SUMS

10.1 REVIEW In Chapter 4 we demonstrated that $3(8) + 3(4)$ can be written as $3(8 + 4)$.

● The number 3 is called the _____ _____ of the expression $3(8) + 3(4)$. Compute the expression $3(8) + 3(4) + 3(9)$ by using 3 as a common factor. In other words, $3(\underline{\hspace{1.5cm}}) = \underline{\hspace{1cm}}$.

common factor

21   63

10.2 COMMON FACTOR In symbols, the number represented by X is a common factor in the expression $XB + XA$.

● If $X = 10$, $B = 3$, and $A = 2$; find $XB + XA$ directly, and then evaluate $X(B + A)$. _____
_____

$10(3) + 10(2) = 50$
$10(3 + 2) = 50$

10.3 COMMON FACTOR Suppose B is equal to X in the expression $XB + XA$. The number represented by X is still a common factor of $X(X) + X(A)$.

● If $X = 10$ and $A = 2$, show that $X(X) + X(A) = X(X + A) = \underline{\hspace{2.5cm}}$.

$10(10) + 10(2) = 120$
$10(10 + 2) = 120$

10.4 COMMON FACTORS Now let's look at the algebraic expression $X^2 + 2XY + Y^2$. The key to the expression $X^2 + 2XY + Y^2$ is the middle term $2XY$. Let's write
$$X^2 + 2XY + Y^2 \text{ as } X^2 + XY + XY + Y^2$$
● $6 + 6 = (\underline{\hspace{1cm}})(6)$
$XY + XY = \underline{\hspace{1cm}}$ times XY

2
2

10.5 COMMON FACTOR Let's look at the first two terms and the last two terms of our expression $X^2 + XY + XY + Y^2$ separately. We have $X^2 + XY$ and $XY + Y^2$. The term $XY + Y^2$ can be factored and rewritten $Y(X) + Y(Y) = Y(X + Y)$.

● What is the common factor of $C^2 + XC$? _____ Rewrite $C^2 + XC$, using the common factor. _____

C
$C(X + C)$

10.6 COMMON FACTORS Using common factors, then, we have $XY + Y^2 = Y(X + Y)$. If $Y = 3$ and $X = 7$, then
$$XY + Y^2 = 3(7) + 3^2 \text{ or } 21 + 9 = 30$$
and $Y(X + Y) = 3(7 + 3) \text{ or } 3(10) = 30$
● What is the common factor of the term $X^2 + XY$?
_____
$$X^2 + XY = \underline{\hspace{1cm}} (X + Y)$$

X

X

10.7 COMMON FACTORS   We have shown that $X^2 + 2XY + Y^2 = X^2 + XY + XY + Y^2 = X(X + Y) + Y(X + Y)$. Notice that $(X + Y)$ is a common factor of the expression $X(X + Y) + Y(X + Y)$.

- Consider $X(X + Y) + Y(X + Y)$.   If $X = 3$ and $Y = 2$, $X + Y = 5$ and $X(X + Y) + Y(X + Y) = X(3 + 2) + Y(3 + 2) = (X + Y)(3 + 2) = (3 + 2)(3 + 2) = (\_\_\_\_)(\_\_\_\_) = \_\_\_\_$.   Therefore $3(3 + 2) + 2(3 + 2) = (3 + 2)(\_\_\_\_)$.

10.8 SQUARE OF $(X + Y)$ The expression $X(X + Y) + Y(X + Y)$ has a common factor $(X + Y)$.   If we separate out this common factor and collect the remaining terms, another $X + Y$, we have $X(X + Y) + Y(X + Y) = (X + Y)(X + Y) = (X + Y)^2$.

- Fill in the missing letters:

$$X^2 + 2XY + \_\_\_\_ = X(X + Y) + \_\_\_\_(X + Y)$$
$$X(X + Y) + Y(_____) = (\_\_\_ + \_\_\_)^2$$
$$(\_\_\_ + \_\_\_)^2 = X^2 + 2XY + Y^2$$

10.9 DEPICTING $(X + Y)$ We can interpret the equation $(X + Y)^2 = X^2 + 2XY + Y^2$ pictorially.   Let's start with two lines, one X units in length and the other Y units in length.

A line $X + Y$ units long can be formed by putting the two segments end to end.

- If X is 2 inches long and Y is 1 inch long, then $X + Y$ is ____ inches long.

10.10 DEPICTING $(X + Y)$ The sum $X + Y$ can be represented by a line $X + Y$ units long.   If we draw a square whose sides are $X + Y$ units long, then the area of this square is the base times the height or $(X + Y)^2$.   In the accompanying illustration, the square with total area $(X + Y)^2$ has been divided into four parts (rectangles).

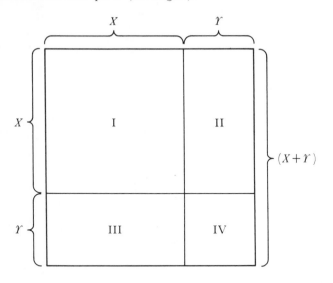

- The area of rectangle III is _____ area units.
  The area of rectangle IV is _____ area units.

XY
Y^2

10.11 DEPICTING $(X + Y)^2$ Considering the total area of the large square in terms of its parts, the square is $X^2 + XY + XY + Y^2$ units in area.
- The middle two terms of $X^2 + XY + XY + Y^2$ can be combined to form the expression $X^2 +$ _____ $+ Y^2$.

$2XY$

10.12 DEPICTING $(X + Y)^2$ Because the length of the figure's side is $X + Y$ units and the figure is a square, its area is $(X + Y)^2$ area units. In symbols,

$$(X + Y)^2 = X^2 + 2XY + Y^2$$

- If $X = 2$ and $Y = 3$, the area of the square is $(2 + 3)^2 =$ _____.
  If $X = 2$ and $Y = 3$ as above, the expression $(X + Y)^2$ can also be computed by adding $X^2 = 4$, $Y^2 = 9$, and $2XY = 12$. Thus $(X + Y)^2$ equals _____.

25

25

B: COMPUTING FORMULA FOR THE VARIANCE

10.13 RELATING $(X + Y)^2$ TO $(X_i - \overline{X})^2$ We have shown algebraically and pictorially that $(X + Y)^2 = X^2 + 2XY + Y^2$ if X and Y are positive numbers. In statistics we frequently encounter expressions such as $(X_i - \overline{X})^2$ (see Chapter 3). Let's change, slightly, the pictorial technique we just developed for $(X + Y)^2$ to find an expression for $(X_i - \overline{X})^2$.

● We could use the formula
$$(X + Y)^2 = X^2 + 2XY + Y^2$$
to express $(X_i - \overline{X})^2$ if we let $X = X_i$ and $Y =$ _____ $\overline{X}$.

minus

10.14 DEPICTING $(X_i - \overline{X})^2$ Consider the illustration:

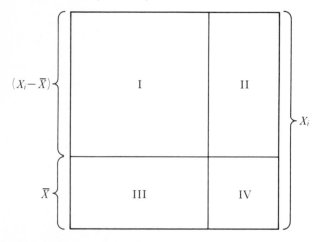

The illustration was formed by taking two lines, one $(X_i - X)$ units long and one $\overline{X}$ units long. When the lines are joined end to end, they form a new line $(X_i - \overline{X}) + (\overline{X}) = X_i$ units long. The figure depicts a large square, with sides X_i units long and area X_i^2. As before, we can break this square into smaller rectangles. Rectangle I has area $(X_i - \overline{X})^2$, and rectangle II has area $\overline{X}(\overline{X}_i - \overline{X})$ area units.

● The height of rectangle III is $\overline{X}$ units long. The base of rectangle III is X_i _____ $\overline{X}$ units long. The area of rectangle III is _____ units. The area of rectangle IV is _____ units. The combined area of the four parts is
$$(X_i - \overline{X})^2 + \overline{X}(X_i - \overline{X}) + \overline{X}(X_i - \overline{X}) + \_\_\_\_$$
$$\overline{X}(X_i - \overline{X}) + \overline{X}(X_i - \overline{X}) = _____$$

minus
$\overline{X}(X_i - \overline{X})$
$\overline{X}^2$

$\overline{X}^2$
$2\overline{X}(X_i - \overline{X})$

10.15 DEPICTING $(X_i - \overline{X})^2$ The length of a whole side of the square in frame 10.14 is X_i. Therefore the area of the whole square is X_i^2 area units.

● $(X_i - \overline{X}) + \overline{X} = \_\_\_\_$.

X_i

10.16 EXPRESSION FOR $(X_i - \overline{X})^2$ We can now write an equation which, when solved, will give us an expression for $(X_i - \overline{X})^2$. Let us look at the equation
$$(X_i - \overline{X})^2 + 2\overline{X}(X_i - \overline{X}) + \overline{X}^2 = X_i^2$$
- To solve this equation for $(X_i - \overline{X})^2$, we must eliminate the terms $\overline{X}^2$ and _____ from the left side of the equation. (Review Section A of Chapter 5, if necessary, for information on solving equations.)

$2\overline{X}(X_i - \overline{X})$

10.17 EXPRESSION FOR $(X_i - \overline{X})^2$ As a first step in solving the equation, we isolate $(X_i - \overline{X})^2$ on the left:
$$(X_i - \overline{X})^2 = X_i^2 - 2\overline{X}(X_i - \overline{X}) - \overline{X}^2$$
Now consider the expression $-2\overline{X}(X_i - \overline{X})$. Since $-2\overline{X}$ is a common factor, we can multiply through by $-2\overline{X}$ to obtain $-2\overline{X}(X_i - \overline{X}) = -2\overline{X}X_i + 2\overline{X}\overline{X}$.
- It is clear that $-2\overline{X}(X_i) = -2\overline{X}X_i$, but the reason $-2\overline{X}(-\overline{X}) = +2\overline{X}\overline{X}$ or simply $2\overline{X}^2$ is that the product of two _____ numbers is a positive number.

negative

10.18 EXPRESSION FOR $(X_i - \overline{X})^2$ Therefore
$$(X_i - \overline{X})^2 = X_i^2 - 2\overline{X}X_i + 2\overline{X}^2 - \overline{X}^2$$
- Add the last two terms together to obtain $(X_i - \overline{X})^2 = X_i^2 - 2\overline{X}X_i + $ _____.

$\overline{X}^2$

10.19 EXPRESSION FOR VARIANCE The resulting equation is
$$(X_i - \overline{X})^2 = X_i^2 - 2\overline{X}X_i + \overline{X}^2$$
Now, suppose we use the Σ sign so that we can compute the expression
$$\sum_{i=1}^{n} (X_i - \overline{X})^2$$
which is needed to find a variance. The formula for the variance is
$$S^2 = \frac{\sum_{i=1}^{n} (X_i - \overline{X})^2}{n-1}$$
- Use the results above to write an alternate formula for the variance:
$$S^2 = \frac{\sum_{i=1}^{n} (\qquad\qquad)}{n-1}$$

$X_i^2 - 2\overline{X}X_i + \overline{X}^2$

10.20 SUMMATION If we sum both sides of the equation
$$(X_i - \overline{X})^2 = X_i^2 - 2\overline{X}X_i + \overline{X}^2$$
from $i = 1$ to n we still have an equation:

$$\sum_{i=1}^{n} (X_i - \overline{X})^2 = \sum_{i=1}^{n} (X_i^2 - 2\overline{X}X_i + \overline{X}^2)$$

● If $n = 3$, $X_1 = 1$, $X_2 = 2$, $X_3 = 3$, and $\overline{X} = 2$, then

$$(X_1 - \overline{X})^2 = (1 - 2)^2 = (-1)^2 = 1$$
$$(X_2 - \overline{X})^2 = (2 - 2)^2 = (0)^2 = 0$$
$$(X_3 - \overline{X})^2 = (3 - 2)^2 = (1)^2 = 1$$

or $\qquad \sum_{i=1}^{3} (X_i - \overline{X})^2 = \underline{\qquad}$

$$X_1^2 - 2\overline{X}X_1 + \overline{X}^2 = 1 - 2(2)(1) + 4 = 1$$
$$X_2^2 - 2\overline{X}X_2 + \overline{X}^2 = 4 - 2(2)(2) + 4 = 0$$
$$X_3^2 - 2\overline{X}X_3 + \overline{X}^2 = 9 - 2(2)(3) + 4 = 1$$

so $\qquad \sum_{i=1}^{3} (X_i^2 - 2\overline{X}X_i + \overline{X}^2) = \underline{\qquad}$

10.21 SUMMATION Using the summation signs, it is possible to simplify the expression

$$\sum_{i=1}^{3} (X_i^2 - 2\overline{X}X_i + \overline{X}^2)$$

This can be rewritten as

$$\sum_{i=1}^{3} X_i^2 - \sum_{i=1}^{3} 2\overline{X}X_i + \sum_{i=1}^{3} \overline{X}^2$$

To see this, add vertically the terms of the example in the previous problem,

$$(X_1^2 - 2\overline{X}X_1 + \overline{X}^2)$$
$$+ (X_2^2 - 2\overline{X}X_2 + \overline{X}^2)$$
$$+ (X_3^2 - 2\overline{X}X_3 + \overline{X}^2)$$

$$(X_1^2 + X_2^2 + X_3^2) - (2\overline{X}X_1 + 2\overline{X}X_2 + 2\overline{X}X_3)$$

$$+ (\overline{X}^2 + \overline{X}^2 + \overline{X}^2) = \sum_{i=1}^{3} X_i^2 - \sum_{i=1}^{3} 2\overline{X}X_i + \sum_{i=1}^{3} \overline{X}^2$$

Note that $(\overline{X}^2 + \overline{X}^2 + \overline{X}^2)$ could also be written as $3\overline{X}^2$ instead of

$$\sum_{i=1}^{3} \overline{X}^2$$

Also, $(2\overline{X}X_1 + 2\overline{X}X_2 + 2\overline{X}X_3)$ could have the common factor $2\overline{X}$ removed and be written as $2\overline{X}(X_1 + X_2 + X_3)$ or

$2\overline{X} \sum_{i=1}^{3} X_i$. Thus

$$\sum_{i=1}^{3} (X_i^2 - 2\overline{X}X_i + \overline{X}^2) = \sum_{i=1}^{3} X_i^2 - 2\overline{X} \sum_{i=1}^{3} X_i + 3\overline{X}^2$$

● If $X_1 = 1$, $X_2 = 2$, $X_3 = 3$, and $\overline{X} = 2$ as before, then

$$\sum_{i=1}^{3} X_i^2 = \underline{\qquad}$$

$$-2\overline{X} \sum_{i=1}^{3} X_i = -(4)(6) = \underline{\qquad}$$

$$3\overline{X}^2 = (3)(2)^2 = \underline{\qquad}$$

and the total is again $\underline{\qquad}$.

2

2

14

-24

12

2

10.22 MEAN The formula for the mean of these observations is

$$\bar{X} = \frac{\sum\limits_{i=1}^{3} X_i}{3}$$

If we multiply both sides of this equation by 3, we have

$$3\bar{X} = \sum_{i=1}^{3} X_i$$

In general,

$$\sum_{i=1}^{n} X_i = n\bar{X}$$

● If $\bar{X} = 2$ and $n = 3$, then $\sum\limits_{i=1}^{3} X_i =$ _____.

6

10.23 SUBSTITUTING $n\bar{X}$ FOR $\sum\limits_{i=1}^{n} X_i$ If we substitute $3\bar{X}$ for $\sum\limits_{i=1}^{n} X_i$ in the formula

$$\sum_{i=1}^{3} X_i^2 - 2\bar{X}\sum_{i=1}^{3} X_i + 3\bar{X}^2$$

we have

$$\sum_{i=1}^{3} X_i^2 - 2\bar{X}(3\bar{X}) + 3\bar{X}^2 = \sum_{i=1}^{3} X_i^2 - 6\bar{X}^2 + 3\bar{X}^2$$
$$= \sum_{i=1}^{3} X_i^2 - 3\bar{X}^2$$

Thus

$$\sum_{i=1}^{3} (X_i - \bar{X})^2 = \sum_{i=1}^{3} X_i^2 - 3\bar{X}^2$$

● For $X_1 = 1$, $X_2 = 2$, $X_3 = 3$, we have

$$\sum_{i=1}^{3} (X_i - \bar{X})^2 = 2$$

But

$$\sum_{i=1}^{3} X_i^2 = 14$$

$$3\bar{X}^2 = 3(2)^2 = 12$$

so

$$\sum_{i=1}^{3} X_i^2 - 3\bar{X}^2 = \underline{\quad}$$

2

10.24 ALTERNATIVE FORMULA FOR $\sum\limits_{i=1}^{n} (X_i - \bar{X})^2$ This formula is valid for any size n, and thus, in general,

$$\sum_{i=1}^{n} (X_i - \bar{X})^2 = \sum_{i=1}^{n} X_i^2 - n\bar{X}^2$$

● If $\sum\limits_{i=1}^{n} (X_i - \bar{X})^2 = 12$, then $\sum X_i^2 - n\bar{X}^2 =$ _____.

12

10.25 ALTERNATIVE FORMULA FOR VARIANCE The formula for the variance given previously was

$$S^2 = \frac{\sum\limits_{i=1}^{n} (X_i - \bar{X})^2}{n-1}$$

Using the results of the previous frames, we can rewrite the variance formula as

$$S^2 = \frac{\sum\limits_{i=1}^{n} X_i^2 - n\overline{X}^2}{n-1}$$

- This alternative formula for S^2 uses a different _____ [numerator, denominator].

10.26 CALCULATION OF VARIANCE   This new formula is useful when the variance is computed on a desk calculator.   It saves time because the mean, $\overline{X}$, does not have to be subtracted from each observation, X_i.   Instead,

$$\sum_{i=1}^{n} X_i \qquad \text{and} \qquad \sum_{i=1}^{n} X_i^2$$

can be found on the calculator, using the cumulative multiplier key.   Then $\overline{X}$ is computed by dividing $\sum\limits_{i=1}^{n} X_i$ by n and this result put directly into the new formula for the variance.

- If $\sum\limits_{i=1}^{n} X_i^2 = 100$, n = 20, and $\overline{X} = 2$, then

$$\begin{aligned}
S^2 &= \frac{\sum\limits_{i=1}^{n} X_i^2 - n\overline{X}^2}{n-1} \\
&= \frac{100 - (20)(2)^2}{19} \\
&= \frac{100 - 80}{19} = \underline{\qquad}
\end{aligned}$$

20/19

10.27 SECOND ALTERNATIVE FOR S^2 We can derive still another formula for the variance which is even easier to compute on a desk calculator.   Let us take the formula in the previous frame,

$$S^2 = \frac{\sum\limits_{i=1}^{n} X_i^2 - n\overline{X}^2}{n-1}$$

and multiply both numerator and denominator by n (this does not change the result).

$$\frac{n}{n} S^2 = \frac{n\left(\sum\limits_{i=1}^{n} X_i^2 - n\overline{X}^2\right)}{n(n-1)} = \frac{n\sum\limits_{i=1}^{n} X_i^2 - n^2\overline{X}^2}{n(n-1)}$$

or $$S^2 = \frac{n\sum\limits_{i=1}^{n} X_i^2 - n^2\overline{X}^2}{n(n-1)}$$

Earlier we showed that

$$n\overline{X} = \sum_{i=1}^{n} X_i$$

Therefore

$$n^2 \overline{X^2} = (n\overline{X})^2 = (\sum_{i=1}^{n} X_i)^2$$

Notice that this is the square of the sum of the X_i from $i = 1$ to n. Using this fact, we obtain

$$S^2 = \frac{n \sum_{i=1}^{n} X_i^2 - (\sum_{i=1}^{n} X_i)^2}{n(n-1)}$$

• In words, the numerator of S^2 is n times the ———— of the squared X_i minus the square of the sum of ————.

sum

X_i

10.28 REVIEW OF VARIANCE FORMULAS   Listed below are the three formulas for the variance.

(1)
$$S^2 = \frac{\sum_{i=1}^{n} (X_i - \overline{X})^2}{n-1}$$

(2)
$$S^2 = \frac{\sum_{i=1}^{n} X_i^2 - n\overline{X}^2}{n-1}$$

(3)
$$S^2 = \frac{n \sum_{i=1}^{n} X_i^2 - (\sum_{i=1}^{n} X_i)^2}{n(n-1)}$$

Formula 1 is the hardest to compute on a desk calculator, but is the easiest to remember and gives the best description of what a variance is. If there are very few observations, and the arithmetic is done by hand, this formula is often the easiest. Formula 2 is easier to compute on a desk calculator and is used a great deal in textbooks. Formula 3 is the fastest to compute on a desk calculator. It is the fastest because $\sum_{i=1}^{n} X_i$ and $\sum_{i=1}^{n} X_i^2$ can be obtained simultaneously by using the cumulative multiplier key, or by locking the long dial. Furthermore, the entire numerator of Formula (3) can be calculated without copying numbers from the dials, because we can multiply n times $\sum_{i=1}^{n} X_i^2$ and multiply $\sum_{i=1}^{n} X_i$ times $\sum_{i=1}^{n} X_i$, using the negative cumulative multiplier key. With this numerator still in the dial of the machine, we then divide by $n(n-1)$ and obtain the variance.

10.29 VARIANCE IS POSITIVE   Using the first formula for the variance,

$$S^2 = \frac{\sum_{i=1}^{n} (X_i - \overline{X})^2}{n-1}$$

we can see that both the numerator (which is a square) and the denominator are always positive. Therefore S^2 is always positive. If you are using any of those formulas given in frame 10.28 to calculate the variance, and you come out with a negative answer, your calculations are incorrect.

● One test for the correctness of your computed value for S^2 is that it must be _____.

Review: Chapter 10

10.1 What are the common factors of the following expressions?

$$4(6) + 4(5) \quad \text{\_\_\_\_}$$
$$XB + XA \quad \text{\_\_\_\_}$$
$$XY + X^2 \quad \text{\_\_\_\_}$$
$$Y^2 + XY \quad \text{\_\_\_\_}$$

4
X
X
Y

10.2 The expression $X^2 + XY + XY + Y^2$ can be split into two parts, $X^2 + XY$ and _____. What is the common factor of both parts? _____
Factoring the common factors out, we have $(X + Y)$ times _____. Therefore $X^2 + XY + XY + Y^2 = ($_____$)^2$.

$XY + Y^2$
$X + Y$

$X + Y$ $X + Y$

10.3 $(X + Y)^2 = X^2 +$ _____ $XY + Y^2$.

2

10.4 Because $\bar{X} = \sum\limits_{i=1}^{n} X_i/n$, we know that

$$\sum_{i=1}^{n} X_i = \text{\_\_\_\_}$$

$n\bar{X}$

If the mean of a group of numbers is zero, what is $\sum\limits_{i=1}^{n} X_i$ equal to? _____

0

10.5 $\dfrac{n}{n} S^2 = $ _____

S^2

10.6 The three formulas for the variance are

$$S^2 = \frac{\sum\limits_{i=1}^{n} (X_i - \bar{X})^2}{n - 1}$$

$$S^2 = \frac{\sum\limits_{i=1}^{n} X_i^2 - n\bar{X}^2}{n - 1}$$

$$S^2 = \frac{n \sum\limits_{i=1}^{n} X_i^2 - (\sum\limits_{i=1}^{n} X_i)^2}{n(n - 1)}$$

With $X_1 = 1$ and $X_2 = 3$, compute the variance, using each of the formulas in succession. _____

2

Preview Questions: Chapter 11

11.1 The difference between the largest and smallest observation is called the _____.

range

11.2 A range of measurements which we are willing to represent by one single measurement is called a _____ _____.

class
interval

11.3 If the end points of a class interval are 5.5 and 10.5, then the midpoint is _____.

8

11.4 If you have a small number of observations, you use _____ (more or fewer) class intervals.

fewer

11.5 The vertical axis on a histogram is called the _____, and the horizontal axis is called the _____.

ordinate
abscissa

11.6 On the ordinate of a histogram the _____ is plotted.

frequency

11.7 On the abscissa of a histogram the _____ of the class intervals are plotted.

midpoints

11.8 Are the following class intervals correct? _____ [yes or no]

no

                140–150 pounds
                151–160 pounds

Chapter

11

Histograms

A graphical representation of data is extremely important in describing research results. The most commonly used descriptive technique is the histogram. Histograms are used in presenting numerical information so that the reader may see the distribution of observations and their typical values. The first section of this chapter explains the concept of class intervals and describes how to construct them. The second section demonstrates how histograms are constructed.

Before starting this chapter, you may wish to review the material on rounding numbers in Chapter 1. The material on frequency tables in Chapter 4 may also be useful, though not necessary.

A: CLASS INTERVALS

11.1 HISTOGRAMS A histogram is a graphical way of describing the data given in a frequency table. In a frequency table, the number of observations having various values are listed. The histogram is a picture of the number of observations having various values.

- One difference between a histogram and frequency table is that a histogram is a _____ and a frequency table is a _____ .

picture
listing

11.2 ROUNDING When making a histogram it is convenient to begin with measurements or data that have been rounded off to the same units. This is particularly important when one uses continuous measurements.

- Round off the following measurements of *height* to the nearest *inch* so that a histogram can be easily constructed.

$X_1 = 70.125$ _____	$X_5 = 71.5$ _____	70	72
$X_2 = 70.6$ _____	$X_6 = 72.0$ _____	71	72
$X_3 = 71.2$ _____	$X_7 = 72.9$ _____	71	73
$X_4 = 71.459$ _____	$X_8 = 74.1$ _____	71	74

11.3 SMALLEST AND LARGEST OBSERVATIONS The next step is to find the smallest and the largest observation. In the previous problem this is simple to do because the smallest measurement, 70 inches, comes first and the largest measurement, 74 inches, comes last. Ordinarily, some searching for the smallest and largest is necessary. However, one is often guided in this search by knowing what values of the observations are feasible.

- From the following three smallest and largest observations of weights of adult males, choose the set you feel is most apt to occur in a sample consisting of male factory workers: (*a*) 190 to 375 pounds, (*b*) 145 to 225 pounds, (*c*) 100 to 150 pounds. _____

(*b*)

11.4 RANGE OF OBSERVATIONS Once you have found the smallest and the largest observation, you next compute their difference, which is called the range.

- If the largest weight is 225 pounds and the smallest 145 pounds, then the range is $225 - 145 =$ _____ pounds.

80

11.5 CLASS INTERVAL The next step is to find a reasonable class interval. By class interval we mean a range of measurements which we would be willing to represent by one single measurement. For example, in the previous problem a class interval might be 10 pounds.

- If we were measuring the height of individuals, would a reasonable class interval be 20 inches? _____ [yes or no]

no

11.6 END POINTS It is important to define the two end points and the midpoint of each class interval. The end points will be the largest and smallest value considered to be in the class interval.

- If you decide that 140.5 is the smallest value and 150.5 is the largest value of a class interval, then these numbers define the _____ _____ of the class interval. The range of this class interval is _____.

end points
10

11.7 MIDPOINT The midpoint is defined as the point in the center of the interval or the average of the two end points.

- The midpoint of 140.5 and 150.5 pounds is _____ pounds.

145.5

11.8 ONE VALUE TO REPRESENT MANY VALUES All the observations in the class interval of 140.5 to 150.5 pounds will be represented by the midpoint 145.5 pounds. In general, all observations falling in a class interval are represented by the midpoint of that class interval.

- With a class interval of 60.5 to 62.5 inches, what number will be used to represent all the observations falling in this class? _____ inches

61.5

11.9 LENGTH OF CLASS INTERVAL The next step is to decide which particular class intervals you should use for your data. If you use very small intervals, you will need many of them. For example, to represent all the observations from 145 to 225 pounds by using a class interval of 1 pound, you would need 80 class intervals.

- Suppose all the observations between 145 and 225 pounds are to be assigned to class intervals. If you use a class interval of 5 pounds, you will need _____ class intervals.

16

11.10 NUMBER OF CLASS INTERVALS Usually we try to represent observations by 8 to 20 class intervals. If the total number of observations is small, then fewer intervals are used. This is done to avoid having class intervals which include no observations.

- If you had a large number of observations, you would probably use _____ [more, fewer] class intervals than if you had a small number of observations.

more

11.11 REASONABLE CLASS INTERVALS Try to choose your class intervals so that the end points and midpoint are reasonable values. For example, end points of 140.5 to 150.5 pounds would be preferred over 143.5 to 153.5 pounds. Frequently, the intervals are dictated by convention to make comparability among studies possible.

- Which of the following sets of class intervals lengths seems more reasonable? (*a*) Intervals of 1, 5, 10, 20, or 100 units length; (*b*) intervals of 3, 7, 13, or 96 units length. _____

(*a*)

11.12 HOW TO FIND CLASS-INTERVAL LENGTH After computing the range of all the observations and counting the number of observations, you can decide on the length of your class intervals. Suppose your smallest observation is 145 pounds and your largest is 225 pounds, and the range is therefore 80 pounds. You want to divide your observations into 8 to 20 class intervals. To obtain an approximate length for the class intervals, divide the range of all the observations by the desired number of class intervals (8 to 20). For example, with a small number of observations, a range of 80 pounds divided by 8 class intervals would yield 10 pounds for the length of each class interval. This is a reasonable number to use.

- If you had heights ranging from 60 to 76 inches and a small number of observations, a reasonable length of a class interval would be _____ divided by _____ or _____ inches.

16   8
2

11.13 CLASS-INTERVAL LENGTH In the example in which the range of all the observations was 80 pounds, if you had a large number of observations and wanted more class intervals, you might use class intervals of 5 pounds. This would give you 80 pounds divided by 5 pounds, or 16 class intervals. The number of class intervals can be estimated by dividing the range of all observations by the length of each class interval. Note that in this case you started with a reasonable size for a class interval and then determined the number of class intervals by dividing the range by the length. In frame 11.12 we started with a reasonable number of intervals and found the length by dividing the range by this number. Either procedure is correct.

- Suppose the range of all the observations is 20 inches and each class interval is to be 2 inches long. In this case the number of class intervals would be _____.

10

11.14 EXACT END-POINT VALUES OF CLASS INTERVALS Once you have rounded your observations, found their range, and estimated the length of each class interval, the next step is to find the exact end-point values of the class intervals. Usually it is easiest to decide on the end points of the lowest class interval first.

- To establish exact end points of class intervals, start with the _____ class interval first.

lowest

11.15 EXACT END-POINT VALUES OF CLASS INTERVALS There are several methods of choosing exact end points, but in this program we shall present only one method. The method we suggest is a general one and can always be used. A necessary property that any set of class intervals must have is that each observation should fall in one and only one class interval. The method discussed in this program will have this property.

- Do the following class intervals have the property that each observation falls into one and only one class interval? _____ [yes or no]

no

    First interval: 70–73 inches
    Second interval: 72–75 inches

11.16 EXACT END-POINT VALUES OF CLASS INTERVALS Let us look at an example of the above property. Suppose we have data on weights which have been rounded off to the nearest whole pound. To make a class interval of length 10 pounds, the following end points would be suitable.

    First interval: 139.5 to 149.5 pounds
    Second interval: 149.5 to 159.5 pounds

Note that each observation, since it is rounded off to the nearest whole pound, can fall in one and only one class interval. If an observation is 149 pounds it goes into the first class interval, if it is 150 pounds it goes into the second class interval.

- Do the following end points have this property? _____ [yes or no]

no

    First interval: 140 to 150 pounds
    Second interval: 150 to 160 pounds

  What is the value of the observation that could fall into either of these two class intervals? ____ pounds. Do the end points given in the above problem result in correct class intervals? _____ [yes or no]

150

no

11.17 EXACT END-POINT VALUES OF CLASS INTERVALS To find exact end points, we should consider the way the observations were rounded off. In the example with weights, the data were rounded off to the nearest whole pound. The exact end points used for a 10-pound class interval were

$$139.5 \text{ to } 149.5 \text{ pounds}$$
$$149.5 \text{ to } 159.5 \text{ pounds}$$

First round off the observations, then add an extra digit to the right of them, which reflects the way in which the data were rounded. In this case a .5 was added to the right of the whole number in pounds, because the data were rounded to the nearest pound.

- The method of finding exact end points is to add an extra _____ to the _____ of the rounded observations. The smallest possible rounded value of the observation in the class interval 139.5 to 149.5 pounds is _____. But 140 pounds represents values ranging from 139.5 to 140.499... pounds. The lowest exact end point of the class interval is _____.

digit   right

140

139.5

11.18 SUCCESSIVE CLASS INTERVALS   Notice that once you have found the first class interval the succeeding ones can be found by adding the length of the class interval to it successively.

- What would be the second and third class interval in the preceding problem?

    Second   _____
    Third   _____

149.5–159.5
159.5–169.5

11.19 MIDPOINTS   The midpoint of each class interval is found by finding the mean of the exact end points. The first class interval is 139.5–149.5 pounds, so the midpoint would be

$$\frac{139.5 + 149.5}{2} = 144.5 \text{ pounds}$$

- What is the midpoint in the second class interval?

$$\frac{149.5 + 159.5}{2} = \underline{\qquad} \text{ pounds}$$

154.5

What is the difference between the midpoint in the first and that in the second class interval? _____ pounds

10

11.20 MIDPOINTS   Once the midpoint for the first class interval is calculated, the other midpoints can be found by adding the length of the class interval successively to the first midpoint.

- What is the midpoint of the third class interval? _____ pounds

164.5

11.21 FREQUENCY TABLE   The information found so far can be summarized in a frequency table.

Frequency table

End points	Midpoints	Frequency
139.5–149.5	144.5	f_1
149.5–159.5	154.5	f_2
159.5–169.5	164.5	f_3
169.5–179.5	174.5	f_4
179.5–189.5	184.5	f_5
189.5–199.5	194.5	f_6
199.5–209.5	204.5	f_7
209.5–219.5	214.5	f_8
219.5–229.5	224.5	f_9

In the column labeled frequency, the number of observations falling in each class interval is listed. When a frequency table is used, all the observations which fall within one class interval are treated as if they had the value listed as the midpoint of that interval.

● In the first interval all the observations are considered to have the value _____ pounds.

144.5

B: DRAWING A HISTOGRAM

11.22 HISTOGRAM   The data given in the frequency table can be used directly to draw a histogram. Your histogram will have a horizontal and a vertical axis. The horizontal axis is called the abscissa and the vertical axis is called the ordinate.

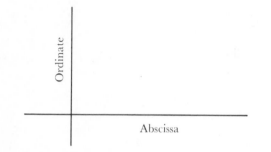

● The axis which is scaled from the bottom to the top is called the _____ axis. The other axis, called the _____ axis, is scaled from _____ to right.

ordinate (or vertical)
abscissa (or horizontal)
left

11.23 HISTOGRAM The midpoints listed in the frequency table are placed on the abscissa. Small values are placed at the left and large values on the right. In this way the abscissa resembles the thermometer used in Chapter 2. The frequencies are placed on the ordinate axis.

- If you were drawing a histogram of the distribution of heights, you would place the _____ of the _____ on the abscissa.

midpoints
heights

11.24 HISTOGRAM Suppose you had the following frequency table of weights in ounces.

| Frequency table | | |
End points	Midpoints	Frequency
19.5–29.5	24.5	2
29.5–39.5	34.5	4
39.5–49.5	44.5	6
49.5–59.5	54.5	6
59.5–69.5	64.5	3
69.5–79.5	74.5	1

First, place the midpoint values on the abscissa. Second, find the largest frequency and scale the ordinate so that there will be room for the largest frequency. In this case the largest frequency is 6, so the top of the ordinate should be near 6. Notice that the ordinate and abscissa are *labeled*, using the proper units of measurement.

- Using the information above, place the correct labels on the following axes.

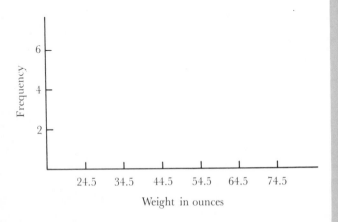

The largest frequency should be allowed for on the _____.

ordinate

11.25 HISTOGRAMS   The next step is to draw in the histogram values.   A rectangle with the height of the frequency and with a base centered on the midpoint is drawn for each class interval.

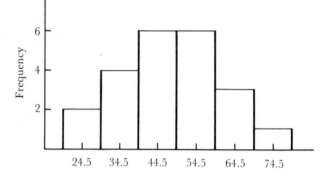

This completes the histogram.

●   We consider the four animals in the interval 29.5–39.5 to be represented by a weight of ＿＿＿＿, and the rectangle for that class interval is centered at ＿＿＿＿. The height of each rectangle is the ＿＿＿＿ of that class interval.   The width of each rectangle is the ＿＿＿＿ of that class interval.

34.5
34.5
frequency

length

11.26 HISTOGRAM   The vertical sides of the rectangle intersect the abscissa at the end points of the class interval.   Thus, if we have equal-length class intervals in the frequency table, we have equal-width rectangles in the histogram.   (Note that histograms constructed with unequal-length class intervals are misleading.)

●   In the histogram pictured in frame 11.25 the vertical line between the two class intervals which have highest frequencies intersects the abscissa at ＿＿＿＿.

49.5

11.27 HISTOGRAM   Frequently, published histograms show midpoint values which have been rounded for ease in interpretation.   For example, age intervals may be represented by midpoints of 25, 35, 45 years, and so on.   In that case, the vertical lines of the rectangles would intersect the abscissa at 20, 30, 40, 50, and so on.

● The following frequency table of weights is rounded to the nearest pound:

End points	Frequency
120.5–140.5	2
140.5–160.5	4
160.5–180.5	3

What are the exact midpoints which would be marked off on the abscissa? _____ _____ _____.

130.5   150.5   170.5

What are the points which might appear in a published histogram? _____ _____ _____.

130   150   170

Review: Chapter 11

11.1   In making a frequency table, the first step after rounding the observations is to find their _____.

range

11.2   If you divide the range of the observations by a number between 8 and 20, you obtain the _____ of the _____ _____.

length   class interval

11.3   The single value used to represent many observations in a class interval is the _____.

midpoint

11.4   You can tell whether an observation is included in an interval by looking at the _____ _____ of the class interval.

end points

11.5   Exact end points have an extra digit added on the _____ side of the number which indicates how the data were rounded off.

right

11.6   Midpoints are defined as the average of the two _____ _____ points.

exact end

11.7   What is plotted on the abscissa of a histogram? _____

midpoints

11.8 What is plotted on the ordinate of a histogram?
_____

frequency

11.9 Once the midpoint of the lowest class interval has been found, successive midpoints can be found by adding the _____ of the _____ _____ successively.

length   class interval

11.10 When drawing a histogram, after marking off midpoints on the abscissa we also label the abscissa with _____ of _____.

units
measurement

11.11 The last step in drawing a histogram is to draw the rectangles with the heights of the _____ and bases centered at the _____.

frequencies
midpoints

Preview Questions: Chapter 12

12.1   From the following list of symbols, choose two which are measurements of the same individual.

$$X_i, X_7, X_n, X_8, Y_7 \qquad \text{\_\_\_\_} \text{\_\_\_\_}$$

12.2   In a scatter diagram, in addition to displaying the numerical value of the observations, one can also display the _____ between the observations.

12.3   Sketch a set of observations which tend to show that high values of X are associated with low values of Y.

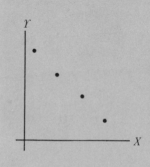

12.4   If you have two pairs of observations with the same X and Y values, then a _____ is plotted on the scatter diagram.

12.5   To construct a two-way frequency table from a scatter diagram, horizontal and vertical lines are drawn at the _____ _____ of the class intervals.

Chapter **12**

Scatter Diagrams and Plotting

Frequently two or more observations are made of the same person or thing. For example, height and weight are often measured on the same individual. The first section of this chapter describes how to display these sets of observations pictorially so that the relationship between observations (e.g., height and weight) can be studied. The second section relates scatter diagrams to the construction of two-way frequency tables. You might wish to review Chapter 2 on subscripted symbols and Chapter 11 on histograms before starting this chapter.

A: DRAWING A SCATTER DIAGRAM

12.1   SYMBOLS   If we have two sets of measurements on each individual, it is convenient to label one measurement with the symbol X and the other with the symbol Y. For example, X_1 could be the height of the first person and Y_1 the weight of the first person.

● The height and weight of the second person would be labeled _____ and _____.

X_2 Y_2

12.2   SUBSCRIPTED SYMBOLS   If we wished to describe the height and weight of an arbitrary person, we would use the subscript i.

● The height and weight of the ith person would be labeled _____ and _____.

X_i Y_i

12.3   SUBSCRIPTED SYMBOLS   As in Chapter 2, the height and weight of the last or nth person in the group can be labeled X_n and Y_n.

● If we have taken ten observations, then $n =$ _____.

10

12.4   SUBSCRIPTED SYMBOLS   The fact that subscripts are *alike* indicates that the observations are taken on the same individual. Thus X_5 and Y_5 should be considered *together* as a set of observations on the fifth person.

● An observation paired with X_{10} might be symbolized as _____.

Y_{10}

12.5   LINKAGE OF OBSERVATIONS   When we had only one observation on each individual, we drew a histogram to get a pictorial representation of our data. We still can do this when we have two observations on each individual by drawing two histograms separately. However, this will not take advantage of the fact that these data were taken in sets of two —for example, that particular heights are linked to particular weights. Each member of the pair is a measurement on the same individual.

● Two separate histograms fail to show that information comes in _____.

pairs or sets

12.6 SCATTER DIAGRAM In order to display all the information we have, we will have to display the *association* between the two types of measurement. This is done in a scatter diagram.

- If we displayed height and weight of the same individuals in two histograms, the information missing would be the _____ between height and weight. The association can be displayed in a _____ _____.

association
scatter diagram

12.7 SCATTER DIAGRAM A scatter diagram is made by drawing a horizontal and a vertical axis. The horizontal axis is frequently labeled the *X* axis, and the vertical axis is labeled the *Y* axis. The following axes (labeled with units of measurement) would be used for a scatter diagram of height and weight.

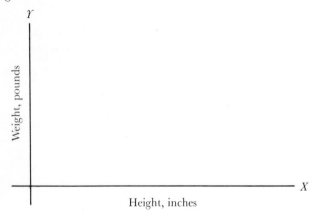

- Height is plotted against the *X* axis or the _____ _____. Weight is plotted against the *Y* axis or the _____. When labeling the axes, the _____ of _____ must be included.

abscissa
(horizontal axis)
ordinate (vertical axis)
units   measurement

12.8 CONTRAST OF HISTOGRAM AND SCATTER DIAGRAM Notice that in Chapter 11, dealing with histograms, the *X* axis might be height but the *Y* axis indicated the frequency of occurrence of different heights and not a separate measurement. Thus, in scatter diagrams, *pairs* of observations are plotted, whereas in histograms, the frequency of a single type of observation is plotted.

- The *Y* axis of the graph of a histogram is always used to describe the _____ of occurrence of the measurement described on the *X* axis. The *Y* axis of a scatter diagram is used to describe one member of a _____ of observations.

frequency

pair

12.9 CONSTRUCTING A SCATTER DIAGRAM   Suppose we had the following observations:

$$X_1 = 10 \text{ inches} \qquad Y_1 = 4 \text{ pounds}$$
$$X_2 = 8 \text{ inches} \qquad Y_2 = 2 \text{ pounds}$$
$$X_3 = 9 \text{ inches} \qquad Y_3 = 3 \text{ pounds}$$
$$X_4 = 8 \text{ inches} \qquad Y_4 = 1 \text{ pound}$$
$$X_5 = 9 \text{ inches} \qquad Y_5 = 2 \text{ pounds}$$

These observations can be displayed on a scatter diagram. The first step is to divide the axes into convenient units covering the range of the observations.

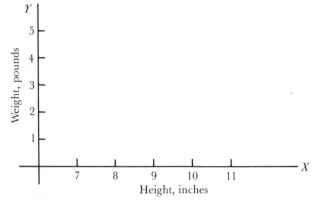

- The units on the horizontal axis range from 7 to 11 inches and the observations, X_i, from ___ to___ inches.

8   10

12.10 CONSTRUCTING A SCATTER DIAGRAM   The next step is to display the observations on the labeled axes. The first set of observations is $X_1 = 10$ inches and $Y_1 = 4$ pounds. We will find 10 inches on the horizontal axis and 4 pounds on the vertical axis. We can draw two lines, one up from 10 inches and the other right from 4 pounds, until these lines intersect. This displays a height of 10 inches and a weight of 4 pounds.

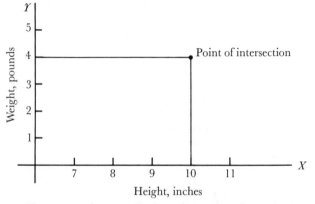

- Place a point to display the pair of measurements $X_2 = 8$ inches, $Y_2 = 2$ pounds.

12.11 CONSTRUCTING A SCATTER DIAGRAM   Once you have the point of intersection, you no longer need the two lines.   The points are usually placed without drawing in the intersecting lines by tracing up and to the right along a ruler or plastic triangle.   The lines are important only for locating a point.
- Each pair of X_i and Y_i results in a single _____.

point

12.12 CONSTRUCTING A SCATTER DIAGRAM   The finished scatter diagram for the five observations given in frame 12.9 would be as follows:

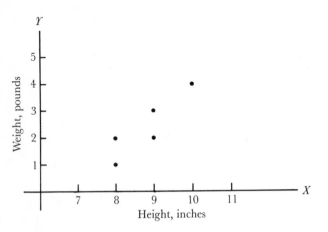

- Add the point $X_i = 10$ inches and $Y_i = 1$ pound to the above scatter diagram.

12.13 DISPLAYING DUPLICATE MEASUREMENTS   If two sets of observations fall at the same point, the number 2 is displayed instead of a dot.
- If there were a 3 at the intersection of 9 inches with 2 pounds, then _____ objects would have had the identical height and weight.

three

12.14 HIGH ASSOCIATION   The points of a scatter diagram also display the *association* between the X observations and the Y observations.   Suppose the X observations were height in *inches* and the Y observations were height in *feet* measured on the same persons.   Then, knowing an X_i observation would automatically tell you the Y_i value.   For example, if a person's height is 60 inches ($X_i = 60$ inches), then $Y_i = 5$ feet.   There is *perfect* or *high association* between these two types of observation.
- If we have accurately measured each person's weight in kilograms and in pounds, then these two sets of observations will be highly _____.

associated

12.15 HIGH ASSOCIATION   The scatter diagram which shows high association could have a pattern such as one of the following.

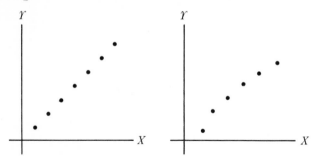

●   Do we have high association in the following scatter diagrams? (a) _____; (b) _____.

(a) yes   (b) no

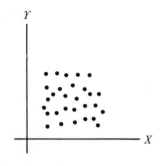

(a)   (b)

12.16 NO ASSOCIATION   When knowing the value of the X observation tells us nothing about the value of the Y observation, we say that no association between X and Y exists. An idealized pattern of no association could be as follows:

- Plot the following two scatter diagrams and indicate the set of observations which has the highest association.

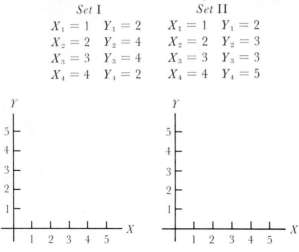

	Set I			Set II	
$X_1 = 1$	$Y_1 = 2$		$X_1 = 1$	$Y_1 = 2$
$X_2 = 2$	$Y_2 = 4$		$X_2 = 2$	$Y_2 = 3$
$X_3 = 3$	$Y_3 = 4$		$X_3 = 3$	$Y_3 = 3$
$X_4 = 4$	$Y_4 = 2$		$X_4 = 4$	$Y_4 = 5$

set II

12.17 ASSOCIATION Usually in real life we look at patterns which are somewhat in between those pictured in frames 12.15 and 12.16. For instance, height and weight in adult males are somewhat associated so we expect a pattern similar to the one below:

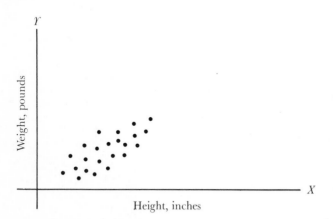

Knowing a person's height gives you some clue to his weight, on the average, but it does not tell you what his exact weight is.

- Would you expect very high association between IQ and grade-point average in school? _____ [yes or no]

no

12.18 DIRECTION OF ASSOCIATION When large values of the X observation are associated with large values of the Y observation and small with small, we expect the array of points to be tilted up on the right-hand side as in frame 12.15.

- If large values of the X observation are associated with small values in the Y observation (for example, income versus proportion of income spent on food by persons) then the array of points will be tilted _____ on the right, as follows:

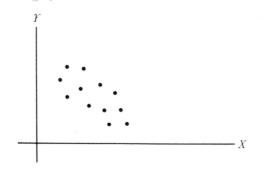

B: MAKING A TWO-WAY FREQUENCY TABLE FROM A SCATTER DIAGRAM

12.19 TWO-WAY FREQUENCY TABLE   If instead of looking at the points, we want actual frequencies, we can make a two-way frequency table from our scatter diagram. We can do this by drawing equally spaced vertical and horizontal lines across our scatter diagram and counting the frequency of observation in each box as follows:

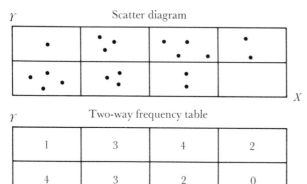

There is a 1 in the upper-left-hand box because only one point occurred in that box in the scatter diagram.

- There are two points in the upper-right-hand box of the scatter diagram and a frequency of _____ in the same place in the two-way frequency table.

2

12.20. TWO-WAY FREQUENCY TABLE The vertical and horizontal lines on the scatter diagram now become a generalization of the end points of the class intervals discussed in Chapter 11. The midpoints fall in the center of the boxes on the scatter diagram.

- If two vertical lines intersect the X axis at 10 and 20, then the X midpoint of these two lines is _____.

15

12.21 ASSOCIATION As in the scatter diagram, if all the frequencies in a two-way frequency table occur in a pattern like the one below, we expect an association between the two sets of observations, X and Y.

Y

		80
	120	
100		

X

- Is there association shown in the following two-way frequency tables?

Y

50		
	85	
		20

X

(a)

yes—negative association

Y

10	10	10
10	10	10
10	10	10

X

(b)

no association

Review: Chapter 12

12.1   In the following set of observations X is weight in ounces and Y is length in inches.

$$X_1 = 5 \quad X_5 = 2 \qquad Y_1 = 3 \quad Y_5 = 2$$
$$X_2 = 4 \quad X_6 = 4 \qquad Y_2 = 2 \quad Y_6 = 3$$
$$X_3 = 2 \quad X_7 = 1 \qquad Y_3 = 2 \quad Y_7 = 1$$
$$X_4 = 2 \quad X_8 = 5 \qquad Y_4 = 1 \quad Y_8 = 2$$

Plot the points and label the following scatter diagram.

See page 128

12.2   Make a two-way frequency table from the scatter diagram you have drawn, using end points of $\frac{1}{2}$, $1\frac{1}{2}$, $2\frac{1}{2}$, and $3\frac{1}{2}$ for the Y axis and 0, 3, and 6 for the X axis.

See page 128

12.3   Is there a high degree of association between X and Y?
_____

no

12.4   Does there seem to be some association?   _____

yes

Answers to Review

12.1

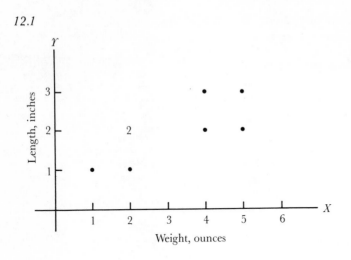

12.2   Two-way frequency table

```
  Y
  ┌─────┬─────┐
  │     │  2  │
  ├─────┼─────┤
  │  2  │  2  │
  ├─────┼─────┤
  │  2  │     │
  └─────┴─────┘ X
```

Preview Questions: Chapter 13

13.1   The logarithm of a number is the _____ to which another number (usually 10) should be raised.

exponent

13.2   If $(3)^A$ times $(3)^B = (3)^C$, then $A + B =$ _____.

C

13.3   The logarithm of the product of two numbers is equal to the _____ of the logarithms.

sum

13.4   Are you familiar with the use of semi-log graph paper? _____ [yes or no]

If no, see Sec. B, Chap. 13

Chapter 13

Logarithms and Log Graph Paper

The final chapter of this book deals with logarithms and the use of graphs involving logarithms. The first section introduces the basic properties of logarithms of numbers, and explains how these properties can be used to perform calculations. The use of log graph paper is described in the second section.

In statistics we frequently work with the logarithms of numbers instead of the numbers themselves because, for many types of observations, the logarithms of the observations have an approximately normal distribution.

A: LOGARITHMS

13.1 EXPONENTIATION In Chapter 8, Section A, exponentiation was defined as repeated multiplication, just as multiplication had been defined as repeated addition.

- The expression $109,232 + 109,232$ can be written as _____ times $109,232$. The expression $(109,232)$ $(109,232)$ can be written as _____.. The expression $(109,232)^1 =$ _____.

2
$(109,232)^2$
$109,232$

13.2 EXPONENTIATION The analogy between multiplication and exponentiation is simple only with whole numbers. For example, it is obvious what is meant by $2(109,232)$ and by $(109,232)^2$. A better understanding of the expression $(109,232)^2$ requires a closer look at the number 2. The number 2 equals $1 + 1$. Also, $(109,232)^2 = (109,232)^1(109,232)^1$. Now what does $(109,232)^3$ mean? One answer is $(109,232)^1$ $(109,232)^1(109,232)^1$, the product of three quantities.

- If $(109,232)^3 = (109,232)^1(109,232)^1(109,232)^1$, and $(109,232^2 = (109,232)^1(109,232)^1$, in what other way can $(109,232)^3$ be written? _____

$(109,232)^2(109,232)^1$

13.3 ADDITION OF EXPONENTS Now, $(109,232)^3$ equals $(109,232)^2(109,232)^1$. Or, we can use symbols and say that $A^3 = (A)^2(A)^1$. In both cases $3 = 2 + 1$, regardless of whether we use $109,232$ or A. As another example, consider 2^6, which equals $(2)(2)(2)(2)(2)(2)$, or 64.

- $2^6 = (2)$— times $(2)^1$
  $B^5 = (B)$— times $(B)^2$

5
3

13.4 ADDITION OF EXPONENTS The multiplication of the number 2 raised to some exponents, 5 and 1, can be achieved by raising 2 to the *sum* of the exponents, that is, to 6. In symbols, the multiplication of 2 raised to some exponents, L and M, can be achieved by considering 2 raised to the *sum* of the exponents, $L + M$.
$$(2)^L(2)^M = 2^{L+M}$$
If we let $K = L + M$, then this can be rewritten as
$$(2)^L(2)^M = 2^K$$
where $K = L + M$. The term 2^K means that K number of 2's are multiplied together.

- The number 8 can be expressed as $(2)(2)(2)$ or 2^3, and the number 4 can be expressed as 2^2. The multiplication of 8 times 4 is equivalent to considering 2 raised to the exponent ____ times 2 raised to the exponent ____. Noting that 8 times $4 = 32$, calculate $[(2)(2)(2)][(2)(2)] = (2^3)(2^2)$ or $2^5 =$ ____

3
2
32

13.5 ADDITION OF EXPONENTS Notice that

$$2^6 = (2)(2)(2) \text{ times } (2)(2)(2) = (2)^3(2)^3$$

or $\qquad (2)(2) \text{ times } (2)(2)(2)(2) = (2)^2(2)^4$

or $\qquad (2) \text{ times } (2)(2)(2)(2)(2) = (2)^1(2)^5$

In general, if $L + M = K$, then $2^K = (2)^L(2)^M$.

● In the situation

$$(2)(2)(2)(2)(2) = (2)(2) \text{ times } (2)(2)(2)$$

what are the values of K, L, and M, in the formula $K = L + M$? ____ ____ ____. Substitute the proper numbers, and check that in this case $K = L + M$.

_____

5   2   3

5 = 2 + 3

13.6 EXPONENT OF 0.5 Now let us turn to the more difficult problem of interpreting the expression $(109,232)^{2.5}$. Because $2.5 = 2 + 0.5$, we have, from the reasoning of the last frames, $(109,232)^{2.5} = (109,232)^2$ times $(109,232)^{0.5}$. We have still to answer the question "What is $(109,232)^{0.5}$?" We know that if $L + M = K$, then

$$(109,232)^K = (109,232)^L \text{ times } (109,232)^M$$

Suppose $K = 1$ and $L = 0.5$ and $M = 0.5$. We see that $L + M$ is equal to $0.5 + 0.5 = 1$, which equals K, and therefore

$$(109,232)^1 = (109,232)^{0.5}(109,232)^{0.5}$$

Notice two things: First, $(109,232)^1$ is just 109,232 itself, so the left-hand side of the above is 109,232. Second, 109,232 equals the product of two quantities which are both written $(109,232)^{0.5}$. In symbols

$$109,232 = (A)(A)$$

where $A = (109,232)^{0.5}$

● The number which, when multiplied by itself, equals 109,232 is called the _____ _____ of 109,232. (If you do not know the answer to the question, see Chapter 8.) The expression $(109,232)^{0.5}$ can be interpreted as _____.

square root

$\sqrt{109,232}$

13.7 EXPONENT OF 0.5 So now we have shown that $(109,232)^{0.5}$ is $\sqrt{109,232}$. What is $(109,232)^{2.5}$? We know that $(109,232)^{2.5} = (109,232)^2(109,232)^{0.5}$. This in turn equals $(109,232)^2$ times $\sqrt{109,232}$.

● If $\sqrt{10}$ is 3.162, then $10^{2.5}$, which equals 10^2 times $\sqrt{10}$, equals ____ times _____ or _____.

100   3.162   316.2

13.8 EXPONENT OF 0.5 To compute the answer to the problem in frame 13.7 we considered $10^{2.5}$ as $(10)^2(10)^{0.5}$ or

(100) (3.162). Therefore $10^{3.5}$ would equal $(10)^3$ (or 1,000) times $(10)^{0.5}$, which is 3,162.

- Compute $10^{4.5}$. _____

  31.62 = 3.162 times _____

  If $10^K = 31.62$, what is K? _____

13.9 EXPONENTS   In the previous problem a K was found so that 10^K would be equal to a given number. Solutions to this type of equation, that is, $10^K = B$, are usually difficult to find, but because of their importance, tables of the solution to this equation were calculated as far back as the sixteenth century. We have already found a few entries for a such a table.

$$10^K = B$$

K	B
0.5	3.162 (or) $10^{.5} = 3.162$)
1.0	10.000 (or $10^1 = 10$)
1.5	31.62
2.0	100.000
2.5	316.2
3.0	1,000.0
3.5	3,162.0
4.0	10,000.0

- Each row of the table relates a number (B) to the _____ to which 10 must be raised to equal B.

13.10 LOGARITHMS   It would be quite logical to call the table a "Table of Exponents," but for historical reasons tables such as this are called "tables of logarithms." The logarithm of a number B is simply the exponent to which another number, say 10, should be raised so that $10^K = B$, where K is defined as the logarithm of B.

- From the table, what is the logarithm of 3162.0? ____

  The logarithm of any number B is the _____ to which another number, say 10, should be raised so $10^K = B$. K is the logarithm of ____.

13.11 LOGARITHMS   Notice that this chapter on logarithms differs from Chapter 8 on squares and square roots. Instead of considering an arbitrary number raised to paticular exponent, 2, we are now considering a particular number, 10, raised to an arbitrary exponent.

- What number occurs in each of the expressions $(1.6)^2$, $(1.9)^2$, and $(0.00087)^2$? ____. What number occurs in each of the expressions $(10)^9$, $(10)^{2.5}$, and $(10)^{.1306}$? ____. Which of the previous two problems relates to logarithms? _____[first or second]

13.12 LOGARITHMS It is convenient to write the solution to equations such as $10^{2.5} = 316.2$ in another symbolic form. In this sense 2.5 is called the logarithm of 316.2, or in symbols, $2.5 = \log 316.2$. Notice that the number 10 does not appear in the expression. Instead, it is understood that the number 2.5 is the exponent of 10.

- Since $\log 3,162.0 = 3.5$, the number _____ to the exponent 3.5 equals 3162.0. When we write $\log 3,162 = 3.5$, what number, pertinent to this equation, is not expressed? _____

10

10

13.13 LOGARITHMS Now what is the practical value of logarithms? The answer depends upon the property defined at the beginning of this chapter, namely, $10^K = (10)^L (10)^M$ is equivalent to $K = L + M$.

- $10^2 = 100$ and $10^{0.5} = 3.162$. Therefore, $10^{2.5}$ or $10^{2+0.5} = (10^2)(10^{0.5}) = (100)(3.162) = $ _____.

316.2

13.14 LOGARITHMS If
$$10^L = 31.62$$
$$10^M = 100.00$$
$$10^K = 3,162$$
then we know that
$$L = \log 31.62$$
$$M = \log 100.00$$
$$K = \log 3,162$$
Now notice that
$$(31.62)(100.00) = 3,162$$
or that $\quad (10)^L (10)^M = (10)^K$
Thus $L + M = K$ or $\log 31.62 + \log 100.00 = \log 3,162$.

- Since $(31.62)(10) = 316.2$, $\log 31.62 + \log$ _____ $=$ $\log 316.2$.

10

13.15 EXCHANGING ADDITION FOR MULTIPLICATION Notice that when one takes logarithms of both sides of an equation which only involves a product such as $BX = Y$, the new equation $\log B + \log X = \log Y$ contains the operation of addition in place of the operation of multiplication.

- In symbols, if $10^L = A$, $10^M = B$, and $10^K = C$ and $AB = C$, then $\log A$ _____ $\log B = \log C$.

$+$

13.16 ADDITIVE PROPERTY OF LOGARITHMS The logarithm of the product of two numbers is equal to the sum of the logarithms of each number.

- $\log (6)(8) = \log 6 + \log$ _____
  $\log 300 = \log 100 + \log$ _____
  If $\log 3 = 0.4771$, then $\log 300 = \log 100 + \log 3 = $
  _____ $+$ _____ $= $ _____.

8
3

2   0.4771   2.4771

Logarithms and   134
Log Graph Paper

13.17 USE OF LOGARITHMS Because it is much easier to add two numbers together than to multiply them, one practical use of logarithms has been to compute products. The results are approximations and depend on the number of digits tabled.

- With the aid of the table in frame 13.9, find the product of 31.62 times 316.2.

$$\log 31.62 = \underline{\hspace{1cm}}$$
$$\log 316.2 = \underline{\hspace{1cm}}$$
$$1.5 + 2.5 = \underline{\hspace{1cm}}$$

Therefore $(31.62)(316.2) = \underline{\hspace{2cm}}$.

1.5
2.5
4.0
10,000

B: LOG GRAPH PAPER

The additive property of logarithms mentioned in the previous frame can be used to simplify computation when many multiplications must be performed. In the age which preceded the invention of the desk calculator, logarithms permitted relatively easy computation. Consequently, extensive tables were made and can be found in collections of mathematical tables. In these tables, the logarithms described in this chapter are called "common logarithms." Instructions for their use are included with the tables.

In elementary statistics, logarithms are important, but not for strictly computational reasons. However, the property that when *A times B* equals *C*, log *A plus* log *B* equals log *C* underlies the statistical importance of logarithms. In the following section, the application of logarithms will be considered in the context of statistical usage. A frequent problem in statistics is the description of population growth.

13.18 POPULATION GROWTH For example, suppose the population of Statistown increases *tenfold* every century. In other words, in year 1400 Statistown had only 100 inhabitants, in year 1500 Statistown would have had a population of 1,000, and in year 1600 the population would have been 10,000.

- In 1700 the number of inhabitants had increased to _____ .

100,000

13.19 RATE OF GROWTH One thing unusual about Statistown's population growth is that the populations at century intervals are round numbers. However, the "rate" of Statistown's population growth is not unrealistic, and it is entirely possible that a country exists whose population has grown as fast as Statistown's. For example, the population of the United States in

1800 was approximately 5,308,000, while in 1900 the population had grown to 75,994,000, or by more than a factor of ten.

- In 1800 Statistown's population was 1,000,000. Its population in 1900, if it continued its previous rate of growth, would have been _____.

10,000,000

13.20 PLOTTING POPULATION GROWTH Let's apply the technique of the previous chapter to obtain a picture of Statistown's population (P) at various dates. Time is plotted on the abscissa and population on the ordinate (see Figure 1).

Figure 1
Population growth of Statistown

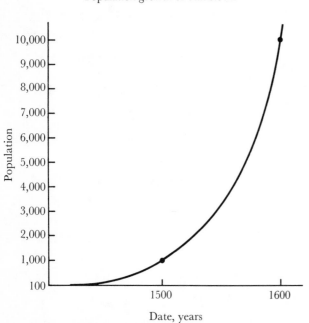

Date, years

- From Figure 1, what was Statistown's approximate population in 1550? _____

between 3,000 and 4,000

13.21 LOGARITHMS Now let's use logarithms to express population as follows:

Date	Population	Population	Log (population)
1500	1,000	10^3	3
1600	10,000	10^4	4
1700	100,000	10^5	5
1800	1,000,000	10^6	6
1900	10,000,000	10^7	7

- If the population in the year 2000 is symbolized as P, and $P = 100,000,000$, then $\log P$ is ___.

8

13.22 PLOTTING LOGARITHMS Now, instead of plotting time on the abscissa and population, P, on the ordinate, let's plot time against log P, as in Figure 2. The graph which had previously been curved now is straight.

Figure 2

Population growth of Statistown in logarithms

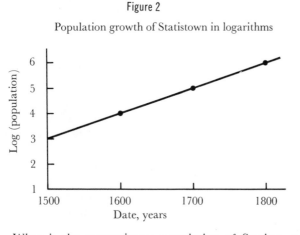

Date, years

● What is the approximate population of Statistown in logarithms at 1550? _____

between 3 and 4

13.23 PLOTTING LOGARITHMS Let us look again at the data plotted in Figures 1 and 2, as given in the table of frame 13.21. We will try to explain why the data plotted in Figure 1 resulted in a curve while that plotted in Figure 2 resulted in a straight line.

● What is the difference, in years, between

1600 and 1500? _____	100 years
1700 and 1600? _____	100 years
1800 and 1700? _____	100 years

What is the difference between successive points if we use the year axis? _____

100 years

What is the difference between

10,000 and 1,000? _____	9,000
100,000 and 10,000? _____	90,000
1,000,000 and 100,000? _____	900,000

Are the differences between successive points the same in the direction of the population axis? _____ What

no

is the difference between successive points in the direction of the log (population) axis? _____ Are the dif-

1

ferences between successive points the same in the direction of the log population axis? _____ Name the

yes

two axes which have constant differences between successive points? _____ and _____

year axis
log (population) axis

13.24 CONDITION FOR A STRAIGHT LINE Whenever there is a constant difference between successive points plotted from both the ordinate and the abscissa, the points will always fall on a straight line. Whenever there are increasing differences between one sequence of points and a constant difference between the other sequence of points, the points follow a curve.

- Would the following set of points result in a straight line? _____ yes

Abscissa value	Ordinate value
1	20
2	40
3	60
4	80

13.25 PLOTTING LOGARITHMS To plot the year against the logarithm of the population, we could use a table of logarithms and find $\log P$ for every P as in Figure 2. An alternative is shown in Figure 3. Notice that in Figure 2 and Figure 3 the lines connecting the points look exactly the same.

Figure 3

Population growth of Statistown

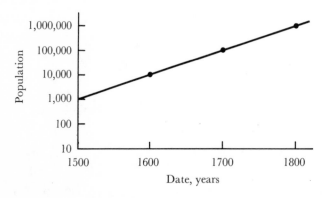

- The only difference between Figure 2 and Figure 3 is that the _____ axis has a different scale. ordinate or Y

13.26 PLOTTING LOGARITHMS The only difference between the steps required for plotting Figure 2 and those for Figure 3 is that the intermediate step of converting the population to logarithms was omitted in Figure 3. Instead of calling the points on the vertical axis 3, 4, 5, and 6, as in Figure 2, we can call them 1,000; 10,000; 100,000; 1,000,000. When graph paper is prepared, as in Figure 3, we need not compute the log (population), because the populations are placed along the ordinate at intervals corresponding to their logs.

- If we use log paper as in Figure 3, is the vertical distance between 1,000 and 10,000 the same as between 10,000 and 100,000? _____ If, instead of using log paper, we find the logs of these numbers and plot the results on *ordinary* graph paper as in Figure 2, will the vertical distance between log (1,000) and log (10,000) be the same as between log (10,000) and log (100,000)? _____

yes

yes

13.27 SEMI-LOG GRAPH PAPER   Notice that when the scale was changed in the previous example, only the ordinate was changed. The abscissa of all the figures was labeled in the usual way. Because only one of the two axes is scaled in logarithms, this graph paper is called semi-log graph paper.

- Semi-log paper has an _____ interval scale on the abscissa.

equal

13.28 SEMI-LOG GRAPH PAPER   Semi-log paper is marked off along the ordinate in sections called cycles. For example, the following is two-cycle log paper (various numbers of cycles are available) :

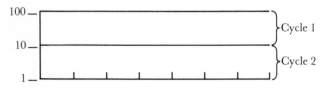

The abscissa is marked off in equal intervals. The ordinate starts with digit 1 followed by a dash, and the next major division is the digit 10 followed by a dash. If the range of numbers to be plotted along the ordinate is 100 to 10,000, we add two zeros to the right of 1___, making it 1<u>00</u>, and similarly for 10<u>00</u> and 100<u>00</u>. Notice that there is *no* zero point on the ordinate.

- If the results to be plotted on the ordinate range from 10 to 1,000, what should the scale making the major sections be labeled? _____ How many cycles would you need to plot numbers ranging from 6 to 1,500 on the ordinate? _____ cycles

10; 100; 1,000

four

Review: Chapter 13

13.1 $2^1 =$ _____.

       2

13.2   What is $(2)^{0.5}$ times $(2)^{0.5}$? _____

       2

13.3   The expression $\sqrt{2}$ can be considered to equal 2 to what exponent? _____

       0.5

13.4   If $(2^L)(2^M) = 2^K$, then $L + M =$ _____.

       K

13.5   If A is any positive number and $(A^L)(A^M) = A^K$, does $L + M = K$? _____

       yes

13.6   If $10^2 = 100$, what is the logarithm of 100? _____ If $10^0 = 1$, what is the logarithm of 1? _____

       2
       0

13.7   When one writes $\log (1{,}000) = 3$, what number, pertinent to the equation, is not expressed? _____

       10

13.8   If $(10^{\log A})(10^{\log B}) = 10^{\log C}$, then $\log A + \log B =$ _____.

       $\log C$

13.9   If $XY = Z$, then $\log X +$ _____ $=$ _____.

       $\log Y$ $\log Z$

13.10   If $10^{\log A} = 100$, what is $\log A$? _____

       2

13.11   Suppose the rabbit population of Australia increased as follows:

10	100	1,000	10,000	100,000
1825	1850	1875	1900	1925

How many rabbits would there probably have been in 1950 if the rate of growth of the rabbit population remained constant? _____

       1,000,000

13.12 If the accompanying sketch represents a piece of semi-log graph paper, sketch the curve of population growth, filling in numbers (and the scales) on the abscissa and ordinate from problem 13.11. Label the axes.

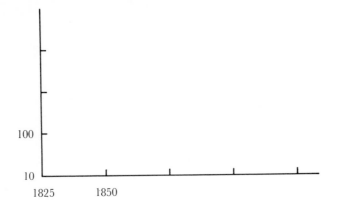

	0	1	2	3	4	5	6	7	8	9
1.0	1.0000	1.0050	1.0100	1.0149	1.0198	1.0247	1.0296	1.0344	1.0392	1.0440
10.	3.1623	3.1780	3.1937	3.2094	3.2249	3.2404	3.2558	3.2711	3.2863	3.3015
1.1	1.0488	1.0536	1.0583	1.0630	1.0677	1.0724	1.0770	1.0817	1.0863	1.0909
11.	3.3166	3.3317	3.3466	3.3615	3.3764	3.3912	3.4059	3.4205	3.4351	3.4496
1.2	1.0954	1.1000	1.1045	1.1091	1.1136	1.1180	1.1225	1.1269	1.1314	1.1358
12.	3.4641	3.4785	3.4928	3.5071	3.5214	3.5355	3.5496	3.5637	3.5777	3.5917
1.3	1.1402	1.1446	1.1489	1.1533	1.1576	1.1619	1.1662	1.1705	1.1747	1.1790
13.	3.6056	3.6194	3.6332	3.6469	3.6606	3.6742	3.6878	3.7014	3.7148	3.7283
1.4	1.1832	1.1874	1.1916	1.1958	1.2000	1.2042	1.2083	1.2124	1.2166	1.2207
14.	3.7417	3.7550	3.7683	3.7815	3.7947	3.8079	3.8210	3.8341	3.8471	3.8601
1.5	1.2247	1.2288	1.2329	1.2369	1.2410	1.2450	1.2490	1.2530	1.2570	1.2610
15.	3.8730	3.8859	3.8987	3.9115	3.9243	3.9370	3.9497	3.9623	3.9749	3.9875
1.6	1.2649	1.2689	1.2728	1.2767	1.2806	1.2845	1.2884	1.2923	1.2961	1.3000
16.	4.0000	4.0125	4.0249	4.0373	4.0497	4.0620	4.0743	4.0866	4.0988	4.1110
1.7	1.3038	1.3077	1.3115	1.3153	1.3191	1.3229	1.3266	1.3304	1.3342	1.3379
17.	4.1231	4.1352	4.1473	4.1593	4.1713	4.1833	4.1952	4.2071	4.2190	4.2308
1.8	1.3416	1.3454	1.3491	1.3528	1.3565	1.3601	1.3638	1.3675	1.3711	1.3748
18.	4.2426	4.2544	4.2661	4.2778	4.2895	4.3012	4.3128	4.3243	4.3359	4.3474
1.9	1.3784	1.3820	1.3856	1.3892	1.3928	1.3964	1.4000	1.4036	1.4071	1.4107
19.	4.3589	4.3704	4.3818	4.3932	4.4045	4.4159	4.4272	4.4385	4.4497	4.4609
2.0	1.4142	1.4177	1.4213	1.4248	1.4283	1.4318	1.4353	1.4387	1.4422	1.4457
20.	4.4721	4.4833	4.4944	4.5056	4.5166	4.5277	4.5387	4.5497	4.5607	4.5717
2.1	1.4491	1.4526	1.4560	1.4595	1.4629	1.4663	1.4697	1.4731	1.4765	1.4799
21.	4.5826	4.5935	4.6043	4.6152	4.6260	4.6368	4.6476	4.6583	4.6690	4.6797
2.2	1.4832	1.4866	1.4900	1.4933	1.4967	1.5000	1.5033	1.5067	1.5100	1.5133
22.	4.6904	4.7011	4.7117	4.7223	4.7329	4.7434	4.7539	4.7645	4.7749	4.7854
2.3	1.5166	1.5199	1.5232	1.5264	1.5297	1.5330	1.5362	1.5395	1.5427	1.5460
23.	4.7958	4.8062	4.8166	4.8270	4.8374	4.8477	4.8580	4.8683	4.8785	4.8888
2.4	1.5492	1.5524	1.5556	1.5588	1.5620	1.5652	1.5684	1.5716	1.5748	1.5780
24.	4.8990	4.9092	4.9193	4.9295	4.9396	4.9497	4.9598	4.9699	4.9800	4.9900

SOURCE: W. J. Dixon and F. J. Massey, Jr., *Introduction to Statistical Analysis*, McGraw-Hill Book Company, New York, 1957.

	0	1	2	3	4	5	6	7	8	9
2.5	1.5811	1.5843	1.5875	1.5906	1.5937	1.5969	1.6000	1.6031	1.6062	1.6093
25.	5.0000	5.0100	5.0200	5.0299	5.0398	5.0498	5.0596	5.0695	5.0794	5.0892
2.6	1.6125	1.6155	1.6186	1.6217	1.6248	1.6279	1.6310	1.6340	1.6371	1.6401
26.	5.0990	5.1088	5.1186	5.1284	5.1381	5.1478	5.1575	5.1672	5.1769	5.1865
2.7	1.6432	1.6462	1.6492	1.6523	1.6553	1.6583	1.6613	1.6643	1.6673	1.6703
27.	5.1962	5.2058	5.2154	5.2249	5.2345	5.2440	5.2536	5.2631	5.2726	5.2820
2.8	1.6733	1.6763	1.6793	1.6823	1.6852	1.6882	1.6912	1.6941	1.6971	1.7000
28.	5.2915	5.3009	5.3104	5.3198	5.3292	5.3385	5.3479	5.3572	5.3666	5.3759
2.9	1.7029	1.7059	1.7088	1.7117	1.7146	1.7176	1.7205	1.7234	1.7263	1.7292
29.	5.3852	5.3944	5.4037	5.4129	5.4222	5.4314	5.4406	5.4498	5.4589	5.4681
3.0	1.7321	1.7349	1.7378	1.7407	1.7436	1.7464	1.7493	1.7521	1.7550	1.7578
30.	5.4772	5.4863	5.4955	5.5045	5.5136	5.5227	5.5317	5.5408	5.5498	5.5588
3.1	1.7607	1.7635	1.7664	1.7692	1.7720	1.7748	1.7776	1.7804	1.7833	1.7861
31.	5.5678	5.5767	5.5857	5.5946	5.6036	5.6125	5.6214	5.6303	5.6391	5.6480
3.2	1.7889	1.7916	1.7944	1.7972	1.8000	1.8028	1.8055	1.8083	1.8111	1.8138
32.	5.6569	5.6657	5.6745	5.6833	5.6921	5.7009	5.7096	5.7184	5.7271	5.7359
3.3	1.8166	1.8193	1.9221	1.8248	1.8276	1.8303	1.8330	1.8358	1.8385	1.8412
33.	5.7446	5.7533	5.7619	5.7706	5.7793	5.7879	5.7966	5.8052	5.8138	5.8224
3.4	1.8439	1.8466	1.8493	1.8520	1.8547	1.8574	1.8601	1.8628	1.8655	1.8682
34.	5.8310	5.8395	5.8481	5.8566	5.8652	5.8737	5.8822	5.8907	5.8992	5.9076
3.5	1.8708	1.8735	1.8762	1.8788	1.8815	1.8841	1.8868	1.8894	1.8921	1.8947
35.	5.9161	5.9245	5.9330	5.9414	5.9498	5.9582	5.9666	5.9749	5.9833	5.9917
3.6	1.8974	1.9000	1.9026	1.9053	1.9079	1.9105	1.9131	1.9157	1.9183	1.9209
36.	6.0000	6.0083	6.0166	6.0249	6.0332	6.0415	6.0498	6.0581	6.0663	6.0745
3.7	1.9235	1.9261	1.9287	1.9313	1.9339	1.9365	1.9391	1.9416	1.9442	1.9468
37.	6.0828	6.0910	6.0992	6.1074	6.1156	6.1237	6.1319	6.1400	6.1482	6.1563
3.8	1.9494	1.9519	1.9545	1.9570	1.9596	1.9621	1.9647	1.9672	1.9698	1.9723
38.	6.1644	6.1725	6.1806	6.1887	6.1968	6.2048	6.2129	6.2209	6.2290	6.2370
3.9	1.9748	1.9774	1.9799	1.9824	1.9849	1.9875	1.9900	1.9925	1.9950	1.9975
39.	6.2450	6.2530	6.2610	6.2690	6.2769	6.2849	6.2929	6.3008	6.3087	6.3166

	0	1	2	3	4	5	6	7	8	9
4.0	2.0000	2.0025	2.0050	2.0075	2.0100	2.0125	2.0149	2.0174	2.0199	2.0224
40.	6.3246	6.3325	6.3403	6.3482	6.3561	6.3640	6.3718	6.3797	6.3875	6.3953
4.1	2.0248	2.0273	2.0298	2.0322	2.0347	2.0372	2.0396	2.0421	2.0445	2.0469
41.	6.4031	6.4109	6.4187	6.4265	6.4343	6.4420	6.4498	6.4576	6.4653	6.4730
4.2	2.0494	2.0518	2.0543	2.0567	2.0591	2.0616	2.0640	2.0664	2.0688	2.0712
42.	6.4807	6.4885	6.4962	6.5038	6.5115	6.5192	6.5269	6.5345	6.5422	6.5498
4.3	2.0736	2.0761	2.0785	2.0809	2.0833	2.0857	2.0881	2.0905	2.0928	2.0952
43.	6.5574	6.5651	6.5727	6.5803	6.5879	6.5955	6.6030	6.6106	6.6182	6.6257
4.4	2.0976	2.1000	2.1024	2.1048	2.1071	2.1095	2.1119	2.1142	2.1166	2.1190
44.	6.6332	6.6408	6.6483	6.6558	6.6633	6.6708	6.6783	6.6858	6.6933	6.7007
4.5	2.1213	2.1237	2.1260	2.1284	2.1307	2.1331	2.1354	2.1378	2.1401	2.1424
45.	6.7082	6.7157	6.7231	6.7305	6.7380	6.7454	6.7528	6.7602	6.7676	6.7750
4.6	2.1448	2.1471	2.1494	2.1517	2.1541	2.1564	2.1587	2.1610	2.1633	2.1656
46.	6.7823	6.7897	6.7971	6.8044	6.8118	6.8191	6.8264	6.8337	6.8411	6.8484
4.7	2.1679	2.1703	2.1726	2.1749	2.1772	2.1794	2.1817	2.1840	2.1863	2.1886
47.	6.8557	6.8629	6.8702	6.8775	6.8848	6.8920	6.8993	6.9065	6.9138	6.9210
4.8	2.1909	2.1932	2.1954	2.1977	2.2000	2.2023	2.2045	2.2068	2.2091	2.2113
48.	6.9282	6.9354	6.9426	6.9498	6.9570	6.9642	6.9714	6.9785	6.9857	6.9929
4.9	2.2136	2.2159	2.2181	2.2204	2.2226	2.2249	2.2271	2.2293	2.2316	2.2338
49.	7.0000	7.0071	7.0143	7.0214	7.0285	7.0356	7.0427	7.0498	7.0569	7.0640
5.0	2.2361	2.2383	2.2405	2.2428	2.2450	2.2472	2.2494	2.2517	2.2539	2.2561
50.	7.0711	7.0781	7.0852	7.0922	7.0993	7.1063	7.1134	7.1204	7.1274	7.1344
5.1	2.2583	2.2605	2.2627	2.2650	2.2672	2.2694	2.2716	2.2738	2.2760	2.2782
51.	7.1414	7.1484	7.1554	7.1624	7.1694	7.1764	7.1833	7.1903	7.1972	7.2042
5.2	2.2804	2.2825	2.2847	2.2869	2.2891	2.2913	2.2935	2.2956	2.2978	2.3000
52.	7.2111	7.2180	7.2250	7.2319	7.2388	7.2457	7.2526	7.2595	7.2664	7.2732
5.3	2.3022	2.3043	2.3065	2.3087	2.3108	2.3130	2.3152	2.3173	2.3195	2.3216
53.	7.2801	7.2870	7.2938	7.3007	7.3075	7.3144	7.3212	7.3280	7.3348	7.3417
5.4	2.3238	2.3259	2.3281	2.3302	2.3324	2.3345	2.3367	2.3388	2.3409	2.3431
54.	7.3485	7.3553	7.3621	7.3689	7.3756	7.3824	7.3892	7.3959	7.4027	7.4095

	0	1	2	3	4	5	6	7	8	9
5.5	2.3452	2.3473	2.3495	2.3516	2.3537	2.3558	2.3580	2.3601	2.3622	2.3643
55.	7.4162	7.4229	7.4297	7.4364	7.4431	7.4498	7.4565	7.4632	7.4699	7.4766
5.6	2.3664	2.3685	2.3707	2.3728	2.3749	2.3770	2.3791	2.3812	2.3833	2.3854
56.	7.4833	7.4900	7.4967	7.5033	7.5100	7.5166	7.5233	7.5299	7.5366	7.5432
5.7	2.3875	2.3896	2.3917	2.3937	2.3958	2.3979	2.4000	2.4021	2.4042	2.4062
57.	7.5498	7.5565	7.5631	7.5697	7.5763	7.5829	7.5895	7.5961	7.6026	7.6092
5.8	2.4083	2.4104	2.4125	2.4145	2.4166	2.4187	2.4207	2.4228	2.4249	2.4269
58.	7.6158	7.6223	7.6289	7.6354	7.6420	7.6485	7.6551	7.6616	7.6681	7.6746
5.9	2.4290	2.4310	2.4331	2.4352	2.4372	2.4393	2.4413	2.4434	2.4454	2.4474
59.	7.6811	7.6877	7.6942	7.7006	7.7071	7.7136	7.7201	7.7266	7.7330	7.7395
6.0	2.4495	2.4515	2.4536	2.4556	2.4576	2.4597	2.4617	2.4637	2.4658	2.4678
60.	7.7460	7.7524	7.7589	7.7653	7.7717	7.7782	7.7846	7.7910	7.7974	7.8038
6.1	2.4698	2.4718	2.4739	2.4759	2.4779	2.4799	2.4819	2.4839	2.4860	2.4880
61.	7.8102	7.8166	7.8230	7.8294	7.8358	7.8422	7.8486	7.8549	7.8613	7.8677
6.2	2.4900	2.4920	2.4940	2.4960	2.4980	2.5000	2.5020	2.5040	2.5060	2.5080
62.	7.8740	7.8804	7.8867	7.8930	7.8994	7.9057	7.9120	7.9183	7.9246	7.9310
6.3	2.5100	2.5120	2.5140	2.5159	2.5179	2.5199	2.5219	2.5239	2.5259	2.5278
63.	7.9373	7.9436	7.9498	7.9561	7.9624	7.9687	7.9750	7.9812	7.9875	7.9937
6.4	2.5298	2.5318	2.5338	2.5357	2.5377	2.5397	2.5417	2.5436	2.5456	2.5475
64.	8.0000	8.0062	8.0125	8.0187	8.0250	8.0312	8.0374	8.0436	8.0498	8.0561
6.5	2.5495	2.5515	2.5534	2.5554	2.5573	2.5593	2.5612	2.5632	2.5652	2.5671
65.	8.0623	8.0685	8.0747	8.0808	8.0870	8.0932	8.0994	8.1056	8.1117	8.1179
6.6	2.5690	2.5710	2.5729	2.5749	2.5768	2.5788	2.5807	2.5826	2.5846	2.5865
66.	8.1240	8.1302	8.1363	8.1425	8.1486	8.1548	8.1609	8.1670	8.1731	8.1792
6.7	2.5884	2.5904	2.5923	2.5942	2.5962	2.5981	2.6000	2.6019	2.6038	2.6058
67.	8.1854	8.1915	8.1976	8.2037	8.2098	8.2158	8.2219	8.2280	8.2341	8.2401
6.8	2.6077	2.6096	2.6115	2.6134	2.6153	2.6173	2.6192	2.6211	2.6230	2.6249
68.	8.2462	8.2523	8.2583	8.2644	8.2704	8.2765	8.2825	8.2885	8.2946	8.3006
6.9	2.6268	2.6287	2.6306	2.6325	2.6344	2.6363	2.6382	2.6401	2.6420	2.6439
69.	8.3066	8.3126	8.3187	8.3247	8.3307	8.3367	8.3427	8.3487	8.3546	8.3606

	0	1	2	3	4	5	6	7	8	9
7.0	2.6458	2.6476	2.6495	2.6514	2.6533	2.6552	2.6571	2.6589	2.6608	2.6627
70.	8.3666	8.3726	8.3785	8.3845	8.3905	8.3964	8.4024	8.4083	8.4143	8.4202
7.1	2.6646	2.6665	2.6683	2.6702	2.6721	2.6739	2.6758	2.6777	2.6796	2.6814
71.	8.4261	8.4321	8.4380	8.4439	8.4499	8.4558	8.4617	8.4676	8.4735	8.4794
7.2	2.6833	2.6851	2.6870	2.6889	2.6907	2.6926	2.6944	2.6963	2.6981	2.7000
72.	8.4853	8.4912	8.4971	8.5029	8.5088	8.5147	8.5206	8.5264	8.5323	8.5381
7.3	2.7019	2.7037	2.7055	2.7074	2.7092	2.7111	2.7129	2.7148	2.7166	2.7185
73.	8.5440	8.5499	8.5557	8.5615	8.5674	8.5732	8.5790	8.5849	8.5907	8.5965
7.4	2.7203	2.7221	2.7240	2.7258	2.7276	2.7295	2.7313	2.7331	2.7350	2.7368
74.	8.6023	8.6081	8.6139	8.6197	8.6255	8.6313	8.6371	8.6429	8.6487	8.6545
7.5	2.7386	2.7404	2.7423	2.7441	2.7459	2.7477	2.7495	2.7514	2.7532	2.7550
75.	8.6603	8.6660	8.6718	8.6776	8.6833	8.6891	8.6948	8.7006	8.7063	8.7121
7.6	2.7568	2.7586	2.7604	2.7622	2.7641	2.7659	2.7677	2.7695	2.7713	2.7731
76.	8.7178	8.7235	8.7293	8.7350	8.7407	8.7464	8.7521	8.7579	8.7636	8.7693
7.7	2.7749	2.7767	2.7785	2.7803	2.7821	2.7839	2.7857	2.7875	2.7893	2.7911
77.	8.7750	8.7807	8.7864	8.7920	8.7977	8.8034	8.8091	8.8148	8.8204	8.8261
7.8	2.7928	2.7946	2.7964	2.7982	2.8000	2.8018	2.8036	2.8054	2.8071	2.8089
78.	8.8318	8.8374	8.8431	8.8487	8.8544	8.8600	8.8657	8.8713	8.8769	8.8826
7.9	2.8107	2.8125	2.8142	2.8160	2.8178	2.8196	2.8213	2.8231	2.8249	2.8267
79.	8.8882	8.8938	8.8994	8.9051	8.9107	8.9163	8.9219	8.9275	8.9331	8.9387
8.0	2.8284	2.8302	2.8320	2.8337	2.8355	2.8373	2.8390	2.8408	2.8425	2.8443
80.	8.9443	8.9499	8.9554	8.9610	8.9666	8.9722	8.9778	8.9833	8.9889	8.9944
8.1	2.8460	2.8478	2.8496	2.8513	2.8531	2.8548	2.8566	2.8583	2.8601	2.8618
81.	9.0000	9.0056	9.0111	9.0167	9.0222	9.0277	9.0333	9.0388	9.0443	9.0499
8.2	2.8636	2.8653	2.8671	2.8688	2.8705	2.8723	2.8740	2.8758	2.8775	2.8792
82.	9.0554	9.0609	9.0664	9.0719	9.0774	9.0830	9.0885	9.0940	9.0995	9.1049
8.3	2.8810	2.8827	2.8844	2.8862	2.8879	2.8896	2.8914	2.8931	2.8948	2.8965
83.	9.1104	9.1159	9.1214	9.1269	9.1324	9.1378	9.1433	9.1488	9.1542	9.1597
8.4	2.8983	2.9000	2.9017	2.9034	2.9052	2.9069	2.9086	2.9103	2.9120	2.9138
84.	9.1652	9.1706	9.1761	9.1815	9.1869	9.1924	9.1978	9.2033	9.2087	9.2141

	0	1	2	3	4	5	6	7	8	9
8.5	2.9155	2.9172	2.9189	2.9206	2.9223	2.9240	2.9257	2.9275	2.9292	2.9309
85.	9.2195	9.2250	9.2304	9.2358	9.2412	9.2466	9.2520	9.2574	9.2628	9.2682
8.6	2.9326	2.9343	2.9360	2.9377	2.9394	2.9411	2.9428	2.9445	2.9462	2.9479
86.	9.2736	9.2790	9.2844	9.2898	9.2952	9.3005	9.3059	9.3113	9.3167	9.3220
8.7	2.9496	2.9513	2.9530	2.9547	2.9563	2.9580	2.9597	2.9614	2.9631	2.9648
87.	9.3274	9.3327	9.3381	9.3434	9.3488	9.3541	9.3595	9.3648	9.3702	9.3755
8.8	2.9665	2.9682	2.9698	2.9715	2.9732	2.9749	2.9766	2.9783	2.9799	2.9816
88.	9.3808	9.3862	9.3915	9.3968	9.4021	9.4074	9.4128	9.4181	9.4234	9.4287
8.9	2.9833	2.9850	2.9866	2.9883	2.9900	2.9917	2.9933	2.9950	2.9967	2.9983
89.	9.4340	9.4393	9.4446	9.4499	9.4552	9.4604	9.4657	9.4710	9.4763	9.4816
9.0	3.0000	3.0017	3.0033	3.0050	3.0067	3.0083	3.0100	3.0116	3.0133	3.0150
90.	9.4868	9.4921	9.4974	9.5026	9.5079	9.5131	9.5184	9.5237	9.5289	9.5341
9.1	3.0166	3.0183	3.0199	3.0216	3.0232	3.0249	3.0265	3.0282	3.0299	3.0315
91.	9.5394	9.5446	9.5499	9.5551	9.5603	9.5656	9.5708	9.5760	9.5812	9.5864
9.2	3.0332	3.0348	3.0364	3.0381	3.0397	3.0414	3.0430	3.0447	3.0463	3.0480
92.	9.5917	9.5969	9.6021	9.6073	9.6125	9.6177	9.6229	9.6281	9.6333	9.6385
9.3	3.0496	3.0512	3.0529	3.0545	3.0561	3.0578	3.0594	3.0610	3.0627	3.0643
93.	9.6437	9.6488	9.6540	9.6592	9.6644	9.6695	9.6747	9.6799	9.6850	9.6902
9.4	3.0659	3.0676	3.0692	3.0708	3.0725	3.0741	3.0757	3.0773	3.0790	3.0806
94.	9.6954	9.7005	9.7057	9.7108	9.7160	9.7211	9.7263	9.7314	9.7365	9.7417
9.5	3.0822	3.0838	3.0854	3.0871	3.0887	3.0903	3.0919	3.0935	3.0952	3.0968
95.	9.7468	9.7519	9.7570	9.7622	9.7673	9.7724	9.7775	9.7826	9.7877	9.7929
9.6	3.0984	3.1000	3.1016	3.1032	3.1048	3.1064	3.1081	3.1097	3.1113	3.1129
96.	9.7980	9.8031	9.8082	9.8133	9.8184	9.8234	9.8285	9.8336	9.8387	9.8438
9.7	3.1145	3.1161	3.1177	3.1193	3.1209	3.1225	3.1241	3.1257	3.1273	3.1289
97.	9.8489	9.8539	9.8590	9.8641	9.8691	9.8742	9.8793	9.8843	9.8894	9.8944
9.8	3.1305	3.1321	3.1337	3.1353	3.1369	3.1385	3.1401	3.1417	3.1432	3.1448
98.	9.8995	9.9045	9.9096	9.9146	9.9197	9.9247	9.9298	9.9348	9.9398	9.9448
9.9	3.1464	3.1480	3.1496	3.1512	3.1528	3.1544	3.1559	3.1575	3.1591	3.1607
99.	9.9499	9.9549	9.9599	9.9649	9.9700	9.9750	9.9800	9.9850	9.9900	9.9950

INDEX